The route to your roots

When they look back at their formative years,
many Indians nostalgically recall the vital part
Amar Chitra Katha picture books have played in their lives.
It was **ACK – Amar Chitra Katha** – that first gave them
a glimpse of their glorious heritage.

Since they were introduced in 1967, there are now **over 400 Amar Chitra Katha**
titles to choose from. **Over 100 million copies** have been sold worldwide.

Now the Amar Chitra Katha titles are even more widely available in **1000+**
bookstores all across India. Log on to www.ack-media.com to locate a bookstore
near you. If you do not have access to a bookstore, you can buy all the titles through our
online store **www.amarchitrakatha.com** We provide quick delivery anywhere in the world.

To make it easy for you to locate the titles of your choice from our
treasure trove of titles, the books are now arranged in six categories.

Epics and Mythology
Best known stories from the Epics and the Puranas

Indian Classics
Enchanting tales from Indian literature

Fables and Humour
Evergreen folktales, legends and tales of wisdom and humour

Bravehearts
Stirring tales of brave men and women of India

Visionaries
Inspiring tales of thinkers, social reformers and nation builders

Contemporary Classics
The Best of Modern Indian literature

Script	Illustrations	Editor
Margie Sastry	Dilip Kadam	Anant Pai

Amar Chitra Katha Pvt Ltd

© Amar Chitra Katha Pvt Ltd, 2000, Reprinted February 2022, ISBN 978-81-8482-223-6
Published by Amar Chitra Katha Pvt. Ltd., AFL House, 7th Floor,
Lok Bharati Complex, Marol Maroshi Road, Andheri (East), Mumbai- 400 059. India
For Consumer Complaints Contact Tel : +91-22 49188881/82/83/84
Email: customerservice@ack-media.com
Printed in India

KRISHNA—THE DARLING OF GOKUL

PAREEKSHIT, THE SON OF ABHIMANYU,* WAS LISTENING WITH RAPT ATTENTION TO THE STORY OF HIS FOREFATHERS NARRATED BY SHUKADEVA.

YOU HAVE TOLD ME ABOUT THE KINGS OF THE SOLAR AND LUNAR DYNASTY. NOW TELL ME, IN DETAIL, THE STORY OF LORD KRISHNA, WHO SAVED ME FROM THE VENGEFUL WRATH OF ASHWATTHAMA, AND WITH WHOSE GRACE MY FOREFATHERS WON THE MAHABHARATA WAR

LISTEN, O PAREEKSHIT, THE STORY OF KRISHNA IS SUCH THAT THE ENQUIRER, THE NARRATOR AND THE LISTENER ARE ALL PURIFIED BY IT.

"LONG, LONG AGO, IN THE DAYS OF YORE, THERE WAS A KING NAMED SHOORASENA OF THE YADAVA RACE, WHO RULED OVER THE KINGDOM OF MATHURA. VASUDEVA WAS HIS SON.

"IN DUE TIME, VASUDEVA WAS MARRIED TO DEVAKI, WITH GREAT POMP.◉

"THE NEWLY WEDS WERE ABOUT TO LEAVE IN THEIR CHARIOT, WHEN...

"...DEVAKI'S COUSIN KAMSA HELD THE REINS IN HIS HAND...

---

* THE SON OF ARJUNA ◉ BY THIS TIME, ACCORDING TO OTHER SOURCES, AFTER THE DEATH OF SHOORASENA THE KINGDOM WAS RULED OVER BY UGRASENA. VASUDEVA HAD RELINQUISHED HIS RIGHT TO THE THRONE, PREFERRING TO BE A COWHERD AND HAD BEEN APPOINTED A MINISTER BY UGRASENA.

"...AND INSISTED ON DRIVING THE CHARIOT HIMSELF.

"FOLLOWING THEM, AT A LITTLE DISTANCE, WERE FOUR HUNDRED CAPARISONED ELEPHANTS, FIFTEEN THOUSAND HORSES, NUMEROUS CHARIOTS CARRYING THE GIFTS BESTOWED ON THE BRIDAL PAIR BY DEVAKI'S FOND FATHER. TWO HUNDRED BEAUTIFULLY BEDECKED MAIDS WERE ALSO IN THE RETINUE.

" SUDDENLY, EVEN AS THE NOTES OF AUSPICIOUS MUSIC REACHED A CRESCENDO, A VOICE RANG OUT FROM THE HEAVENS.

BEWARE, YOU FOOL! THE EIGHTH-BORN OF THIS VERY WOMAN WILL SLAY YOU!

" THE CRUEL KAMSA, ABLAZE WITH ANGER AND FRIGHT, DREW HIS SWORD.

I WILL KILL HER RIGHT AWAY!

" VASUDEVA INTERVENED —

STOP KAMSA! YOU ARE THE GLORY OF YOUR RACE. MIGHTY WARRIORS RELATE STORIES OF YOUR VALOUR.

IT DOES NOT BECOME YOU TO KILL DEVAKI, A WOMAN, YOUR OWN COUSIN AND THAT TOO ON HER WEDDING DAY.

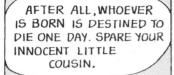

AFTER ALL, WHOEVER IS BORN IS DESTINED TO DIE ONE DAY. SPARE YOUR INNOCENT LITTLE COUSIN.

" VASUDEVA TRIED HIS BEST TO DISSUADE KAMSA WITH PRAISE AND REASONING, BUT IN VAIN—

I MUST SAVE POOR DEVAKI'S LIFE NOW. I WILL PROMISE TO GIVE MY SONS TO HIM. WHO KNOWS, PERHAPS MY SON MAY REALLY KILL HIM. PERHAPS KAMSA HIMSELF MAY BE DEAD SOON, BEFORE ANY SON IS BORN.

" ALOUD HE SAID—

YOU HAVE NO REASON TO FEAR THIS DAMSEL. ACCORDING TO THE CELESTIAL VOICE, IT IS HER SONS WHO POSE A THREAT TO YOU. I PROMISE I WILL BRING EVERY CHILD TO YOU AS SOON AS IT IS BORN.

" KAMSA KNEW HE COULD TRUST VASUDEVA'S WORDS.

I BELIEVE YOU, AND SPARE DEVAKI'S LIFE. BUT BE SURE TO KEEP YOUR PROMISE.

" VASUDEVA AND DEVAKI RETURNED HOME. MONTHS ROLLED BY AND ONE DAY —

KAMSA. HERE IS MY FIRST-BORN, KIRTIMAN. AS I PROMISED, I HAVE BROUGHT HIM TO YOU.

OH! TAKE THIS LITTLE ONE AWAY. IT IS YOUR EIGHTH CHILD WHO IS SUPPOSED TO KILL ME.

AS YOU SAY.

" VASUDEVA WAS NOT FULLY CONVINCED.

WHATEVER HE MAY SAY, I CANNOT TRUST KAMSA. HE MAY CHANGE HIS MIND ANY TIME.

MEANWHILE NARADA VISITED KAMSA.

KAMSA. TAKE CARE. DEVAKI, VASUDEVA, NANDA, IN FACT, ALL THE INHABITANTS OF BRAJA ARE INCARNATIONS OF THE DEVAS. THEY HAVE DESCENDED TO EARTH TO RID IT OF CRUEL OPPRESSORS.

I HAD BETTER BE WARY OF THE SONS OF DEVAKI.

CAPTURE VASUDEVA AND DEVAKI. THROW THEM INTO PRISON, TIGHTLY BOUND IN IRON CHAINS.

" KAMSA NOW BEGAN TO REVEAL HIMSELF IN HIS TRUE COLOURS. HE PUT HIS FATHER UGRASENA IN PRISON, AND TOOK OVER THE KINGDOM. AMONG HIS FRIENDS WERE THE WICKED ASURAS— PRALAMBA BAKA, CHANURA AND TRINAVARTA.

" KAMSA PROVED TO BE A STRONG BUT CRUEL KING. HE HAD THE SUPPORT OF JARASANDHA, THE EMPEROR WHO RULED FROM MAGADHA. BECAUSE OF HIS OPPRESSIVE RULE, HIS SUBJECTS BEGAN TO FLEE THE KINGDOM TO TAKE SHELTER IN OTHER PARTS OF THE COUNTRY.

" MEANWHILE, ONE BY ONE, ALL THE SONS BORN TO DEVAKI, WERE PUT TO DEATH BY KAMSA.

" WHEN HER SEVENTH CHILD WAS DUE, DEVAKI'S HAPPINESS WAS AGAIN CLOUDED OVER BY APPREHENSIONS.

OH! HOW CRUEL IS THE FATE THAT AWAITS OUR CHILD. KAMSA WILL SURELY KILL IT AT BIRTH.

SHUKADEVA EXPLAINED TO PAREEKSHIT—

ALTHOUGH SHE WAS NOT AWARE OF IT, DEVAKI'S SEVENTH CHILD WAS NONE OTHER THAN SHESHA, ON WHOM LORD VISHNU RECLINES. LORD VISHNU INSTRUCTED YOGAMAYA*, TO TRANSFER THE BABY FROM DEVAKI TO ROHINI, VASUDEVA'S SECOND WIFE WHO WAS IN GOKUL.

LATER, ON THE VERY DAY THAT LORD VISHNU WOULD BE BORN AS THE EIGHTH SON OF DEVAKI, YOGAMAYA WAS TO TAKE BIRTH AS YASHODA'S DAUGHTER.

"ON DIVINE COMMAND, YOGAMAYA CAUSED THE UNBORN BABY TO BE TRANSFERRED FROM DEVAKI'S WOMB TO THAT OF ROHINI'S.

"AS A RESULT, ROHINI FOUND HERSELF WITH CHILD JUST WHEN DEVAKI LOST HER BABY. IN DUE TIME ROHINI GAVE BIRTH TO A SON.

"BEFORE LONG, DEVAKI FOUND HERSELF EXPECTING HER EIGHTH CHILD. HER RADIANT BEAUTY SHONE THROUGH THE BARS OF THE JAIL LIKE THAT OF A LAMP CONCEALED IN AN EARTHEN POT.

"EVEN KAMSA NOTICED THE STRANGE GLOW ON DEVAKI'S FACE.

DEVAKI NEVER LOOKED LIKE THIS BEFORE. SURELY IT IS THE PRESENCE OF VISHNU HIMSELF INSIDE HER THAT MAKES HER SO RADIANT.

BUT WHAT CAN I DO? IF I KILL HER NOW, I WILL NEVER BE ABLE TO LIVE DOWN THE STIGMA OF KILLING A WOMAN, MY OWN COUSIN AND THAT TOO WHEN SHE IS WITH CHILD.

"IMPATIENTLY KAMSA WAITED FOR THE BIRTH OF DEVAKI'S EIGHTH CHILD.

ORDER THE GUARDS TO LET ME KNOW THE MOMENT THE BABY IS BORN.

"AT LAST THE AUSPICIOUS DAY DAWNED. THE ENTIRE UNIVERSE SEEMED TO CELEBRATE THE EVENT.

"VASUDEVA WAS FILLED WITH WONDER ON BEHOLDING THE NEW-BORN BABY. IT HELD ALOFT A MACE, A DISC, A CONCHSHELL AND A LOTUS IN HIS FOUR TINY HANDS. HIS BEAUTIFUL DUSKY COMPLEXION CONTRASTED VIVIDLY WITH THE YELLOW SILK ENVELOPING HIM.

"WITH FOLDED HANDS, VASUDEVA FELL ON HIS KNEES AND BEGAN TO PRAY TO HIS DIVINE SON.

LORD! YOU HAVE TAKEN BIRTH IN OUR HOUSE IN ORDER TO PROTECT THE EARTH. BUT THE CRUEL KAMSA WILL HASTEN TO DESTROY YOU AS SOON AS HE HEARS THE NEWS.

"DEVAKI TOO WAS FILLED WITH AWE AT THE SIGHT OF HER BABY.

I KNOW, LORD, THAT YOU WILL BE OUR SAVIOUR. BUT DO NOT LET KAMSA SEE YOU IN THIS DIVINE FORM, I BESEECH YOU!

"IN THE TWINKLING OF AN EYE THE BABY ASSUMED THE FORM OF AN ORDINARY NEW-BORN.

KAMSA MUST NOT SET EYES ON THIS SON OF OURS. I MUST TAKE HIM AWAY. BUT HOW?

"NO SOONER HAD HE THOUGHT TO HIMSELF THUS THAN—

OH! MY CHAINS AND FETTERS HAVE FALLEN OFF! DEVAKI, GIVE THE CHILD TO ME. QUICK!

"TENDERLY HOLDING THE BABY IN HIS ARMS, VASUDEVA STEPPED OUT OF THE ROOM.

"MIRACULOUSLY HE FOUND THE PRISON DOORS WIDE OPEN AND THE GUARDS ALL BLISSFULLY ASLEEP. UNDETECTED, HE WALKED OUT WITH THE BABY.

"IT WAS A DARK, STORMY NIGHT. THE RIVER YAMUNA WAS IN SPATE.

I WOULD LIKE TO GO TO GOKUL ACROSS THE RIVER, TO MY FRIEND NANDA. BUT WHO WILL TAKE ME ACROSS THESE STORMY WATERS?

" AND, LO AND BEHOLD, THE RIVER WATERS PARTED.

"ON REACHING GOKUL, HE FOUND ALL THE PEOPLE DEEP IN SLUMBER.

"ON REACHING NANDA'S HOUSE, HE PLACED HIS BABY BOY BY THE SIDE OF YASHODA, NANDA'S WIFE, AND PICKED UP HER NEW-BORN DAUGHTER.

"IT WAS ONLY AFTER VASUDEVA HAD GONE AWAY THAT YASHODA BECAME AWARE OF THE CHILD NEXT TO HER. SHE, LIKE THE REST OF THE PEOPLE OF GOKUL HAD BEEN UNDER A TRANCE SINCE HER BABY WAS BORN.

"MEANWHILE VASUDEVA RETURNED TO THE PRISON IN MATHURA. HE PLACED THE BABY GIRL BY THE SIDE OF DEVAKI.

I'LL PUT THE FETTERS BACK ON MY FEET. THE DOORS ARE LOCKED AS BEFORE. NO ONE WILL GUESS I HAVE BEEN AWAY.

"AT DAWN, THE LUSTY CRIES OF THE CHILD WOKE UP THE THE GUARDS.

DID YOU HEAR THAT? GO AT ONCE AND INFORM THE KING.

"KAMSA WAS HASTILY WOKEN UP. HE RUSHED TO THE PRISON.

THE EIGHTH-BORN! MY WOULD-BE SLAYER!

"WHEN KAMSA ARRIVED THERE, DEVAKI IMPLORED HIM—

MY DEAR BROTHER, PLEASE SPARE THIS CHILD. SURELY YOU WOULD NOT KILL A FEMALE? ALLOW ME TO KEEP THIS LAST CHILD OF MINE.

"BUT KAMSA WAS UNMOVED. HE SEIZED THE BABY BY HER TINY LEGS...

"...AND DASHED HER AGAINST A STONE SURFACE.

"BUT THIS WAS NO ORDINARY BABY. THE DIVINE INFANT ROSE TOWARDS THE SKY AND MANIFESTED HERSELF AS AN EIGHT-ARMED GODDESS.

"ADDRESSING KAMSA, SHE SAID—

YOU FOOL! THE ONE WHO IS DESTINED TO DESTROY YOU STILL LIVES! DO NOT KILL OTHER INNOCENT INFANTS.

"THEN SHE DISAPPEARED.

"KAMSA WAS WONDERSTRUCK ON HEARING THIS PROCLAMATION. IN A DAZE, HE RELEASED DEVAKI AND VASUDEVA.

MY DEAR SISTER, WHAT A GREAT SINNER I HAVE BEEN TO KILL MY NEPHEWS. I REALLY REGRET MY ACTIONS.

"BUT HIS REPENTANCE WAS SHORT-LIVED. NEXT MORNING HE CALLED FOR HIS MINISTERS AND CRONIES TO RELATE THE EVENTS OF THE NIGHT.

...SO I LET VASUDEVA AND DEVAKI GO SINCE THE DIVINE BEING SAID THAT THE ONE WHO IS DESTINED TO KILL ME IS BORN ELSEWHERE.

"HIS WICKED ASURA FRIENDS SAID —

O KING, IF THAT IS SO, WE WILL SEARCH EVERYWHERE IN THE KINGDOM AND KILL ALL INFANTS WHO ARE TEN DAYS OLD OR LESS.

"KAMSA AGREED. ADDRESSING A RAKSHASI CALLED POOTANA, HE SAID —

POOTANA, GO TO EVERY VILLAGE AND CITY, AND KILL ALL THE NEW-BORN BABIES.

"MEANWHILE, AT GOKUL, NANDA WAS OVERJOYED AT THE BIRTH OF A SON TO HIM AND CELEBRATED IT WITH DUE CEREMONY.

"THE PEOPLE OF GOKUL WERE EAGER TO SEE THE SON OF THEIR CHIEF BEDECKED IN THEIR BEST GARMENTS, THE GOPAS* AND GOPIKAS, AS THEY WERE CALLED, MADE THEIR WAY TO NANDA'S PALACE.

"THEY CROWDED AROUND TO HAVE A LOOK AT THE BABY.

GOD BLESS THIS BOY.

MAY HE LIVE LONG!

WHAT A BEAUTIFUL FACE HE HAS!

"THE GOPAS CELEBRATED THE EVENT WITH GAY ABANDON, SPRINKLING ONE ANOTHER WITH MILK AND CURDS, AND SMEARING BUTTER ON ONE ANOTHER'S FACES.

* COWHERDS

"NANDA GAVE GENEROUS GIFTS TO HIS VISITORS.

"AFTER FEW DAYS, LEAVING GOKUL IN THE HANDS OF OTHER COWHERDS, NANDA WENT TO MATHURA TO PAY HIS ANNUAL DUES TO KAMSA.

"WHEN VASUDEVA HEARD OF HIS ARRIVAL, HE HASTENED TO MEET HIM.

"AFTER EMBRACING HIM AFFECTIONATELY, VASUDEVA SAID—

HOW FORTUNATE YOU TWO ARE TO GET A SON AFTER ALL THESE YEARS.

IT IS A PITY THAT WE SELDOM MEET. YOU AND YOUR WIFE LOOK AFTER ROHINI AND MY SON. I HOPE HE IS WELL AND LOOKS UPON YOU AS HIS PARENTS.

SO MANY OF YOUR SONS WERE KILLED BY KAMSA. EVEN YOUR LITTLE DAUGHTER DID NOT SURVIVE. VERILY, OUR LIFE IS GOVERNED BY DESTINY.

"VASUDEVA SAID— NOW THAT YOU HAVE PAID YOUR ANNUAL DUES AND MET ME TOO, YOU MUST NOT TARRY HERE ANY LONGER. MANY CALAMITIES ARE LIKELY TO DESCEND ON GOKULA.

"ON VASUDEVA'S ADVICE, NANDA MADE HIS WAY HOME.

WHY DID VASUDEVA SAY SUCH A THING, I WONDER. BUT HIS WORDS CAN NEVER BE FALSE. MAY GOD PROTECT US.

"WHILE NANDA WAS AWAY, THE WICKED POOTANA REACHED GOKUL IN THE FORM OF A BEAUTIFUL DAMSEL.

"SHE FOUND HER WAY INTO NANDA'S HOME AND BEHELD THE SLEEPING KRISHNA.

"SHE LIFTED HIM UP IN HER ARMS. BOTH ROHINI AND YASHODA WERE SURPRISED TO SEE THIS STRANGER, BUT WERE SO CARRIED AWAY BY HER BEAUTY THAT THEY DID NOT ASK ANY QUESTIONS.

"POOTANA TOOK THE BABY IN HER LAP AND BEGAN TO SUCKLE HIM.

AH! THE DEADLY POISON THAT I HAVE SMEARED ON MY BREASTS WILL SOON TAKE EFFECT!

"BUT LITTLE DID SHE KNOW THAT IT WAS HER LIFE THAT WAS IN DANGER. FOR THE INFANT, KRISHNA, SOON BEGAN TO SUCK THE VERY LIFE OUT OF HER.

AIEEE!! LET GO! LEAVE ME!

"SHE SHRIEKED AND SHRIEKED. UNABLE TO BEAR THE PAIN, SHE ASSUMED HER UGLY RAKSHASI FORM, AND COLLAPSED IN A HEAP.

" BUT STILL KRISHNA WOULD NOT LET GO OF HER. THE PETRIFIED GOPIKAS HASTILY PULLED HIM AWAY AND TOOK HIM TO YASHODA.

" YASHODA ANOINTED AND BATHED KRISHNA AND ROCKED HIM TO SLEEP.

" WHEN NANDA AND HIS COMPANIONS RETURNED TO GOKUL, THEY WERE SURPRISED TO SEE POOTANA'S HIDEOUS SUPINE FORM.

WHAT VASUDEVA PROPHESIED HAS COME TRUE. HOW AMAZING !

" HE WAS ALL THE MORE ASTONISHED WHEN HE HEARD THAT IT WAS HIS KRISHNA WHO HAD TORMENTED AND KILLED POOTANA. HE PICKED UP HIS LITTLE SON AND KISSED HIM ON HIS FOREHEAD AGAIN AND AGAIN.

" NANDA AND YASHODA WATCHED THEIR SON GROW WITH DELIGHT. WHEN HE LEARNT TO TURN ON HIS SIDE, THE EVENT WAS CELEBRATED WITH SONG AND FEASTING.

"ALL THE PEOPLE OF GOKUL HAD GATHERED AT NANDA'S HOUSE. SEEING THAT THE BABY WAS A LITTLE TIRED AFTER ALL THE FUSS, YASHODA FED HIM AND MADE HIM SLEEP.

"PLACING HIS COT IN THE SHADE OF A CART, SHE WENT BACK TO HER GUESTS.

"AFTER A BRIEF NAP, KRISHNA WOKE UP AND BEGAN TO CRY. BUT YASHODA WAS TOO FAR AND TOO BUSY TO HEAR HIM.

"LOUDER AND LOUDER HE CRIED AND KICKED UP HIS BABY FEET IN THE AIR.

"BUT THE TOUCH OF THE TINY FEET WAS ENOUGH.

"THE NOISE OF THE VESSELS BREAKING BROUGHT THE GUESTS TO THE SPOT.

SEE! THAT CART HAS OVERTURNED ON ITS OWN!

ALL THAT FOOD IS WASTED.

MAYBE THE CART WAS OVERLOADED.

"THE SMALL BOYS WHO WERE PLAYING NEARBY SAID—

IT WAS THE LITTLE ONE. HE KICKED THE CART.

WE SAW IT! WE SAW IT!

"BUT NO ONE BELIEVED THEM.

IS IT POSSIBLE FOR A BABY TO TOPPLE SUCH A HEAVY CART?

DON'T LISTEN TO THEM. LITTLE BOYS ARE ALWAYS IMAGINING THINGS.

"YASHODA HAD MEANWHILE TAKEN THE BABY AWAY AND SOOTHED HIM. SLOWLY, PEOPLE WENT BACK TO THEIR FEASTING AND THE MATTER WAS FORGOTTEN FOR A WHILE.

"A FEW DAYS LATER, YASHODA WAS SITTING WITH KRISHNA IN HER LAP.

WHY! HE SUDDENLY FEELS SO HEAVY. I CAN HARDLY BEAR HIS WEIGHT.

"SHE PLACED HIM ON THE GROUND AND WAS SOON ENGROSSED IN HOUSEHOLD WORK.

"KRISHNA WAS HAPPILY PLAYING AND GURGLING ON HIS OWN. SUDDENLY—

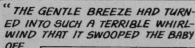

" THE GENTLE BREEZE HAD TURN-
ED INTO SUCH A TERRIBLE WHIRL-
WIND THAT IT SWOOPED THE BABY
OFF.

"IT WAS TRINAVARTA, ANOTHER EVIL ASURA FRIEND OF KAMSA,
WHO HAD APPEARED IN THE GUISE OF A WHIRLWIND TO
DESTROY KRISHNA.

" THE ENTIRE GOKUL WAS
FILLED BY DUST AND DARK-
NESS. NO ONE COULD SEE
ANYTHING.

" YASHODA CAME RUNNING OUT.

OH! WHERE IS MY
DARLING BABY? I HAD
LEFT HIM HERE JUST
NOW!

" WHEN THE WHIRLWIND HAD
SUBSIDED—

WHAT
HAPPENED,
YASHODA?

MY SON!
HE HAS JUST
DISAPPEARED!

" MEANWHILE AS THE WICKED
TRINAVARTA CARRIED THE BABY SKY-
WARDS, HE FOUND HIM BECOMING
HEAVIER AND HEAVIER.

"KRISHNA'S WEIGHT COMPELLED THE DEMON TO SLOW DOWN NOW KRISHNA CAUGHT HIM BY THE THROAT...

"...AND KILLED HIM.

" DOWN FELL THE DEMON TO HIS DEATH.

AHHH!

" THE PEOPLE OF GOKUL WATCHED THE SCENE WITH OPEN-EYED AMAZEMENT.

"ONCE AGAIN KRISHNA WAS RESCUED AND RESTORED TO HIS ANXIOUS MOTHER.

THANK GOD YOU ARE SAFE.

HOW RIGHT VASUDEVA WAS! STRANGE THINGS ARE HAPPENING HERE.

" ONE DAY, GARGA, THE FAMILY PRIEST OF THE YADAVAS, VISITED GOKUL AT VASUDEVA'S BIDDING.

"AFTER WELCOMING HIM WITH DUE RESPECT, NANDA SAID —

WE ARE HONOURED BY YOUR VISIT, GARGACHARYA. MAY I REQUEST YOU TO CONDUCT THE NAMING CEREMONY OF OUR TWO BOYS?

"GARGA EXPLAINED —

I AM THE ROYAL PRIEST OF THE YADAVAS. IF THE NEWS OF MY PERFORMING THE CEREMONY OF THE BOYS REACHES KAMSA, HE WILL BE SUSPICIOUS.

EVER SINCE HE HEARD THAT HIS SLAYER HAS BEEN BORN ELSEWHERE, KAMSA HAS BEEN ON THE LOOKOUT FOR HIM. HE WOULD SURELY HAVE YOUR SON KILLED.

"NANDA SAID —

IN THAT CASE WE WILL DO EVERYTHING ON THE QUIET. NOT EVEN MY NEAR ONES WILL KNOW OF IT.

"SO IN ABSOLUTE SECRECY, WITHOUT ANY FANFARE, THE NAMING CEREMONY OF THE TWO BOYS WAS PERFORMED IN A COWSHED.

THIS SON OF ROHINI, WILL BE A CHARMING BOY, PLEASING PEOPLE WITH HIS GOOD QUALITIES. HENCE HE SHOULD BE CALLED RAMA. BECAUSE OF HIS PROWESS, HE WILL BE CALLED BALARAMA.*

YOUR OTHER DUSKY COMPLEXIONED SON WILL BE CALLED KRISHNA, BECAUSE OF HIS COLOUR. HE WILL BRING PLEASURE AND PROSPERITY TO YOU. TAKE GOOD CARE OF HIM.

"IN A FEW WEEKS BALARAMA AND KRISHNA LEARNT TO CRAWL. NOW THERE WAS NO STOPPING THE TWO BOYS. THEY WOULD WANDER ALL OVER GOKUL, DRAGGING THEIR LITTLE FEET ADORNED WITH ANKLETS THROUGH THE MUDDY PASTURES.

"THEIR CHILDISH PRANKS WERE A CONSTANT SOURCE OF AMUSEMENT TO THEIR MOTHERS.

YASHODA! COME AND SEE YOUR KRISHNA.

WHAT IS HE UP TO NOW?

*BALA = STRENGTH.

"THE FRIGHTENED CALF RAN HELTER SKELTER.

SEE! HE'S BEING DRAGGED AWAY BY THE CALF.

JUST LOOK AT HIS FACE! HE'S ENJOYING IT!

" ROHINI AND YASHODA COULD NEVER BE SURE WHAT THE NAUGHTY PAIR WOULD DO NEXT.

YASHODA DEAR! THE HOUSE IS SO QUIET. THOSE TWO MUST BE UP TO SOME MISCHIEF! WILL YOU GO AND LOOK?

YES, I WILL! I HOPE THEY HAVEN'T CAUGHT HOLD OF A DOG IN THE STREET AS THEY DID THE OTHER DAY.

OR TRIED TO PICK UP A SWORD LIKE YESTERDAY!

"SOON YASHODA WAS BACK, DRAGGING THE TWO WITH HER.

YOU WERE RIGHT, ROHINI! I CAUGHT THEM JUST IN TIME, TRYING TO PEEP INTO THE WELL ON TIPTOE.

WHAT WILL THEY THINK OF NEXT?

"SOON KRISHNA AND BALARAMA LEARNT TO WALK AND RUN.

KRISHNA! BALARAMA! I SHOULD KEEP THEM TIED UP, I THINK! WHERE COULD THEY BE?

" SHE KNEW SOON ENOUGH.

YASHODA, YOU MUST CONTROL THAT NAUGHTY SON OF YOURS.

WHAT HAPPENED?

" EVERY DAY THERE WOULD BE FRESH COMPLAINTS FROM THE NEIGHBOURS.

HE ATE UP ALL THE BUTTER IN MY HOUSE!

AND HE BROKE THE POT ALSO.

HE IS ALL OVER OUR HOUSE. WHEN WE SCOLD HIM, HE JUST GIGGLES AND RUNS AWAY.

HE STEALS THE BUTTER AND GIVES IT TO HIS MONKEY FRIENDS.

"EVERYDAY, THE NAUGHTY KRISHNA WOULD THINK OF NEW WAYS TO STEAL BUTTER WHICH WOULD BE KEPT OUT OF HIS REACH.

"YASHODA WOULD MAKE UP HER MIND TO SCOLD HIM.

JUST LET HIM COME HOME TODAY!

"BUT ONE LOOK AT HIS WIDE-EYED INNOCENT FACE WOULD MELT HER HEART.

"ONE DAY, KRISHNA AND BALARAMA WERE PLAYING IN THE FIELDS WITH THEIR FRIENDS. SOON, BALARAMA CAME RUNNING HOME.

MA YASHODA! KRISHNA HAS EATEN EARTH!

YES! YES! WE SAW HIM.

YOU NAUGHTY BOY! WHY DID YOU EAT EARTH?

THEY ARE TELLING LIES. I DID NOT EAT ANY.

LET ME SEE. OPEN YOUR MOUTH WIDE.

"YASHODA WAS GRIPPED BY AWE.

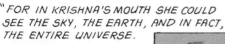

"FOR IN KRISHNA'S MOUTH SHE COULD SEE THE SKY, THE EARTH, AND IN FACT, THE ENTIRE UNIVERSE.

SURELY I MUST BE DREAMING.

IS IT MY EGO THAT MAKES ME THINK LIKE THIS? HELP ME, GOD!

BUT SOON SHE MIRACULOUSLY FORGOT THE WHOLE INCIDENT.

"ANOTHER DAY—

ALL THE MAIDS ARE BUSY, BUT I MUST HAVE FRESH BUTTER MADE FOR MY KRISHNA. HMM, I WILL CHURN IT MYSELF.

"SHE WAS BUSY SINGING AND WORKING.

"KRISHNA HEARD HIS MOTHER SINGING MELODIOUSLY AND CLIMBED ONTO HER LAP.

"YASHODA WAS ENGROSSED IN THE CHILDISH PRATTLE OF KRISHNA WHEN SUDDENLY—

OH! THE MILK MUST HAVE BOILED OVER!

"KRISHNA DID NOT LIKE THIS AT ALL. HE BROKE THE CHURNING POT IN ANGER. WITH TEARS IN HIS EYES AND A CONTAINER OF BUTTER IN HIS HAND, HE MARCHED OFF...

"...TO A SAFE CORNER TO EAT THE STOLEN BUTTER IN PEACE.

"WHEN YASHODA CAME BACK—

THE POT IS BROKEN! IT MUST BE KRISHNA. JUST LET ME CATCH HOLD OF HIM.

"BY NOW KRISHNA'S HUNGER AND ANGER HAD BOTH GONE. SHE FOUND HIM STANDING ON AN UPTURNED MORTAR HAPPILY SHARING THE BUTTER WITH THE MONKEYS.

AS SOON AS HE SAW YASHODA, KRISHNA RAN AWAY WITH HIS FRIENDS.

RUN! RUN! MA HAS A STICK IN HER HAND.

"YASHODA WAS QUITE OUT OF BREATH BY THE TIME SHE MANAGED TO CATCH HOLD OF KRISHNA.

TODAY, I MUST PUNISH YOU. YOU ARE BECOMING NAUGHTIER EVERY DAY!

"SHE DRAGGED HIM BACK HOME.

I WILL BIND YOU UP TO THE SAME MORTAR.

AHH! HERE IS SOME ROPE! NOW AT LEAST I WILL KNOW WHERE YOU ARE.

WHY! THIS ROPE IS SHORT BY JUST TWO FINGERS. ROHINI! GET SOME ROPE!

OH DEAR! AGAIN THIS IS A LITTLE SHORT FOR TYING A KNOT.

"THERE WAS A LOOK OF MISCHIEF ON KRISHNA'S TEAR-STAINED FACE, AS IF HE WAS AMUSED AT HER FINDING THE ROPE SHORT. BUT AT LAST SHE MANAGED TO TIE HIM UP FIRMLY.

NOW YOU WILL STAY HERE TILL I DECIDE TO FREE YOU.

"BUT SHE WAS MISTAKEN. AS SOON AS HER BACK WAS TURNED—

I'LL FIND SOMEONE. TO UNTIE ME.

"SLOWLY DRAGGING THE HEAVY MORTAR WITH HIM", HE TRUDGED ON TOWARDS THE BANK OF THE RIVER.

"ON HIS WAY WERE TWO YAMALARJUNA* TREES. KRISHNA MANAGED TO GO IN BETWEEN, BUT THE MORTAR GOT STUCK.

"WHEN KRISHNA TUGGED AT THE ROPE TO PULL HIMSELF FREE, BOTH THE TREES WERE UPROOTED...

* TWIN TREES OF THE GENUS, TERMINALIA

"...AND CAME CRASHING TO THE GROUND.

CRASH

SHUKADEVA PAUSED HERE DURING HIS NARRATION TO EXPLAIN TO PAREEKSHIT THE DIVINITY OF KRISHNA.

OUT OF THE TWO FALLEN TREES SPRANG TWO SHINING BEINGS. THEY FOLDED THEIR HANDS BEFORE KRISHNA. THEY WERE IN FACT, NALAKUBERA AND MANIGREEVA WHO HAD BEEN UNDER A CURSE AND WERE NOW RELEASED BECAUSE OF THIS ACT OF KRISHNA.

"THE LOUD CRASH BROUGHT PEOPLE RUNNING TO THE SCENE.

WHAT WAS THAT?

MAYBE LIGHTNING HAS STRUCK!

BUT THERE IS NO THUNDER!

" WHEN THEY REACHED THE SPOT—

HOW DID THESE HUGE TREES FALL?

WHAT IS KRISHNA DOING HERE?

ODD THINGS ARE ALWAYS HAPPENING WHEN THIS BOY IS AROUND.

IT WAS KRISHNA WHO MADE THE TREES FALL!

WE SAW HIM DO SO!

AND TWO SHINING FIGURES CAME OUT OF THE TREES.

DON'T LISTEN TO THEIR CHILDISH TALK! SUCH IMAGINATION!

"SOON VASUDEVA TOO CAME THERE AND UNTIED THE ROPE BINDING KRISHNA. BUT SUCH PUNISHMENTS DID NOT DETER LITTLE KRISHNA FROM HIS MISCHIEVOUS WAYS. HE WOULD BE ALWAYS OUT OF THE HOUSE, SINGING AND DANCING TO AMUSE THE GOPIKAS.

ALL MY HOUSEWORK IS STILL TO BE DONE BUT THIS BOY IS SUCH FUN TO WATCH!

"HIDING PEOPLE'S THINGS WAS ANOTHER FAVOURITE PRANK OF HIS. BUT, WHATEVER HE DID, THE PEOPLE OF GOKUL WOULD NEVER FAIL TO BE ENCHANTED AT THE SIGHT OF HIS BEAUTIFUL FACE. ONE DAY—

I'LL GIVE A FISTFUL OF GRAIN IN EXCHANGE FOR THE FRUIT.

FRESH FRUIT!

"BUT BY THE TIME KRISHNA RAN OUT. ALL THE GRAIN FELL THROUGH HIS TINY FINGERS.

OH! WHERE DID IT ALL GO?

NEVER MIND! HERE, HOLD THIS PROPERLY.

" AS KRISHNA RAN AWAY HAPPILY WITH HIS BOOTY—

WHAT IS THIS? MY BASKET IS FILLED WITH GEMS! WHAT A MIRACLE!

"THE OLDER HE GREW, THE MORE TIME KRISHNA SPENT ON THE RIVER BANK, FROLICKING WITH HIS FRIENDS.

KRISHNA! BALARAMA! COME HOME QUICKLY. YOU HAVE NOT EATEN SINCE MORNING.

I CAN HARDLY RECOGNIZE YOU UNDER ALL THAT MUD! GO AND HAVE A BATH. SEE HOW CLEAN YOUR FRIENDS ARE!

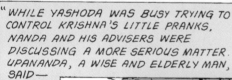

"WHILE YASHODA WAS BUSY TRYING TO CONTROL KRISHNA'S LITTLE PRANKS, NANDA AND HIS ADVISERS WERE DISCUSSING A MORE SERIOUS MATTER. UPANANDA, A WISE AND ELDERLY MAN, SAID—

SUCH CALAMITIES HAVE BEGUN TO HAPPEN IN OUR QUIET GOKUL. I FEEL IT IS TIME TO LEAVE THIS PLACE FOR THE WELFARE OF OUR YOUNG ONES.

SEE THAT LITTLE DARLING OF NANDA. WHAT MIRACULOUS ESCAPES HE HAS HAD. FIRST THAT WICKED POOTANA, THEN THE CART FALLING ON HIM, THAT HORRIBLE WHIRLWIND PICKING HIM UP AND DASHING HIM DOWN. AND THOSE TWO TREES FALLING! THANK GOD NO ONE WAS INJURED.

"AFTER COLLECTING THEIR CATTLE, THE PEOPLE OF GOKUL LOADED THEIR CARTS WITH THEIR BELONGINGS. THE WOMEN, CHILDREN AND THE AGED, ALL RODE ON CHARIOTS AND CARTS. WITH THEIR BOW AND ARROW IN HAND, THE YOUNG MEN WALKED BESIDE THEM. WITH A SONG ON THEIR LIPS, AND HOPE IN THEIR HEARTS, THE PEOPLE OF GOKUL SET OUT IN SEARCH OF A NEW HOME.

KRISHNA: THE SUBDUER OF KALIYA

SHUKADEVA, THE SON OF SAGE VYASA, WAS TELLING PAREEKSHIT, THE GRANDSON OF ARJUNA, THE STORY OF KRISHNA.

YOU MEAN ALL THE PEOPLE OF GOKUL LEFT THE PLACE TOGETHER?

YES, THE ELDERS OF THE CLAN THOUGHT IT WAS WISER TO LEAVE GOKUL. KRISHNA, THE BELOVED SON OF THEIR LEADER, HAD BEEN INVOLVED IN TOO MANY MISHAPS IN GOKUL. SO THEY ALL WENT TO VRINDAVAN TO SETTLE THERE.

" THEY FOUND VRINDAVAN TO BE A BEAUTEOUS SPOT IN LUSH SURROUNDINGS. MOUNT GOVARDHAN LOOMED AT A DISTANCE, AND THE RIVER YAMUNA, WITH ITS GRASSY BANKS, FLOWED GENTLY PAST.

" THE NEW SETTLERS FIRST BUILT SHEDS FOR THE CATTLE...

"...AND SOON SETTLED DOWN AFTER BUILDING THEIR OWN HOMES.

"BALARAMA AND KRISHNA WERE DELIGHTED TO BE IN VRINDAVAN. IN THEIR SWEET VOICES THEY WOULD OFTEN PRAISE THEIR NEW PLACE.

"THEY WISHED TO EXPLORE THE FOREST AROUND.

MAY I ALSO GO TO GRAZE THE COWS?

NO! YOU ARE TOO SMALL TO GO TO THE FOREST.

BUT I SO MUCH WISH TO GO, MA!

ALL RIGHT. YOU AND BALARAMA MAY TAKE THE CALVES TO GRAZE. BUT DON'T GO TOO FAR!

"WHILE THE CALVES GRAZED THE TENDER GRASS CONTENTEDLY, THE BOYS WOULD BE ENGROSSED IN GAMES.

"THEY PLAYED THEIR FLUTES AND DANCED TO THE RHYTHM OF THEIR ANKLETS...

"...OR THEY WOULD PRETEND TO BE BULLS FIGHTING.

"ONE DAY, KRISHNA AND HIS FRIENDS WERE HERDING THEIR CATTLE TOGETHER ALONG THE BANKS OF THE YAMUNA. SUDDENLY KRISHNA STOPPED TO STARE AT SOMETHING HE HAD SEEN.

BALARAMA! SEE THAT BLACK CALF! SURELY HE IS NOT ONE OF OURS.

YES, HE LOOKS A LITTLE ODD.

SHH! LET US APPROACH HIM QUIETLY FROM BEHIND.

"IN REALITY IT WAS A DEMON IN DISGUISE. KRISHNA STEALTHILY APPROACHED THE CALF AND...

"...HOLDING HIS HIND LEGS FIRMLY IN ONE HAND, TWIRLED HIM AROUND.

"THEN WITH A TWIST OF HIS WRIST HE THREW THE DEMON CALF ON TO THE TOP OF A WOOD-APPLE TREE.

"THE DEMON REGAINED HIS TRUE FORM AS HE FELL TO HIS DEATH, CRUSHING A NUMBER OF TREES UNDER HIS WEIGHT.

"KRISHNA'S OTHER COMPANIONS BECAME EXCITED AS THEY SAW IT.

WELL DONE!

AHA! WHAT A FEAT!

"WHEN THEY WERE A LITTLE OLDER, KRISHNA AND BALARAMA WERE ALLOWED TO TAKE THE OLDER CATTLE TO THE FOREST TO GRAZE.

"THEY WOULD CARRY THEIR MORNING MEAL WITH THEM, AND ROAM ALL DAY, FROM FOREST TO FOREST, WITH THEIR HERD. ONE DAY—

COME, LET US DRIVE THE COWS TOWARDS THE LAKE. THEY MUST BE THIRSTY NOW.

"WHEN THE COWS HAD QUENCHED THEIR THIRST, SUDDENLY —

LOOK THERE!

WHAT A HUGE CRANE!

"PERCHED BESIDE THE WATER WAS A CRANE. STRONG AND HUGE, IT POUNCED ON KRISHNA AND PICKED HIM UP IN ITS SHARP BEAK.

"EVEN AS KRISHNA'S COMPANIONS STARED OPEN-MOUTHED WITH SHOCK, THE CREATURE SWALLOWED KRISHNA AT ONE GULP.

"SO TERRIFIED WERE THE COWHERDS THAT THEY FAINTED FROM SHOCK.

"BUT AS SOON AS KRISHNA REACHED DOWN THE MOUTH OF THE DEMON, THE CREATURE FELT AN UNBEARABLE HEAT INSIDE HIS THROAT...

"...AND QUICKLY SPEWED OUT HIS VICTIM.

" THE CRANE WAS NONE OTHER THAN BAKASURA, A FRIEND OF KAMSA. ENRAGED, HE ATTACKED KRISHNA WITH HIS SHARP BEAK.

" NOW KRISHNA SPRANG UP GRABBED THE CREATURE...

"... AND PLAYFULLY TORE IT APART.

" WHEN THEY REGAINED CONSCIOUSNESS, THE COWHERDS WERE OVERJOYED TO HAVE THEIR PLAYMATE BACK AND HUGGED HIM AFFECTIONATELY.

COME, GATHER THE CATTLE NOW. LET US GO BACK HOME.

"THEY HURRIED HOME TO RELATE THE INCIDENT TO THEIR PARENTS. THE GOPAS AND GOPIKAS GATHERED TOGETHER TO HEAR THE TALE.

...AND KRISHNA TORE THE DEMON APART AS IF HE WERE TEARING UP A TINY REED.

WE WERE SO RELIEVED TO SEE HIM SAFE!

"THE ELDERS WERE AMAZED.

ONCE AGAIN THIS BOY HAS ESCAPED FROM THE JAWS OF DEATH.

WHOEVER TRIES TO HARM THIS BOY ALWAYS COMES TO HARM HIMSELF.

GARGACHARYA WAS RIGHT. THIS BOY IS INDEED GREAT.

"KRISHNA AND BALARAMA SPENT THEIR DAYS HAPPILY FROLICKING AND PLAYING WITH OTHER COWHERDS. EARLY AT DAWN THEY WOULD LEAVE THEIR HOMES WITH THEIR HERD...

"...AND SPEND THE DAY SPORTING IN THE FOREST AND FIELDS. THEY WOULD ADORN THEMSELVES WITH WILD FLOWERS, FRESH BLOSSOMS AND PEACOCK FEATHERS..."

"...OR PLAY A GAME OF HIDE AND SEEK..."

"...OR PLAY MUSIC ON THEIR FLUTES AND PIPES..."

"...OR RACE ONE ANOTHER.

COME! LET'S SEE WHO CAN RUN AND TOUCH KRISHNA FIRST.

"THEY WOULD IMITATE THE SOUNDS OF THE FOREST.

BUZZ ZZZZ

HMM MM

COOO! COOO!

COOHOO! COOHOO!

"...OR IMITATE THE BIRDS' WALK AND DANCE.

SEE! I AM AS GRACEFUL AS A SWAN.

I AM A PEACOCK. SEE MY DANCE.

"WITH THE MONKEYS OF THE JUNGLE, THEY WOULD SCAMPER UP THE TREES AND LEAP FROM ONE BRANCH TO ANOTHER.

"ONE DAY, WHEN THE COWHERDS WERE PLAYING THEIR SIMPLE GAMES AGHASURA, A DREADFUL DEMON SAW THEM.

HOW HAPPILY THEY ARE PLAYING HERE, AS IF THEY ARE JUST INNOCENT CHILDREN.

BUT AMONG THEM IS THAT BOY KRISHNA WHO KILLED MY SISTER POOTANA AND MY BROTHER BAKASURA.

TODAY I WILL KILL HIM AND ALL HIS FRIENDS.

"AGHASURA, WHO WAS STRONG ENOUGH TO TERRIFY EVEN THE DEVAS, ASSUMED THE FORM OF AN ENORMOUS SERPENT.

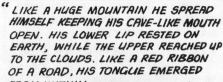

"LIKE A HUGE MOUNTAIN HE SPREAD HIMSELF KEEPING HIS CAVE-LIKE MOUTH OPEN. HIS LOWER LIP RESTED ON EARTH, WHILE THE UPPER REACHED UP TO THE CLOUDS. LIKE A RED RIBBON OF A ROAD, HIS TONGUE EMERGED FROM WITHIN."

"WHEN THE COWHERDS SAW THE CREATURE IN THEIR PATH, THEY WERE AMAZED.

SEE THIS ODD CREATURE. IT LOOKS LIKE A PYTHON WAITING TO SWALLOW US!

HA! HA! SEE HOW THE RAYS OF THE SUN ARE TURNING THE CLOUDS PINK.

THEY LOOK LIKE HIS UPPER JAW.

"INNOCENTLY THEY SAID —

AND THE SHADOW OF THOSE CLOUDS IS ALSO RED. THAT MUST BE HIS LOWER LIP.

SEE THIS LONG RED-HUED ROAD. IT LOOKS LIKE THE TONGUE OF A SERPENT!

HOW HOT THE WIND IS! THERE MUST BE A FOREST FIRE NEAR BY!

AND SUCH A STENCH TOO! SOME POOR CREATURES MUST HAVE BEEN BURNT IN THE FIRE!

"ONCE INSIDE AGHASURA'S MOUTH, KRISHNA BEGAN TO GROW...

"....AND GROW AND GROW.

"NOW AGHASURA COULD NOT BREATHE. HIS THROAT WAS CHOKED, HIS EYE-BALLS BULGED OUT, AND SOON HIS ENORMOUS BODY BECAME LIFELESS.

"KRISHNA, THE COWHERDS AND THE CATTLE STEPPED OUT UNSCATHED FROM THE DEAD DEMON'S MOUTH.

"AFTER SOME TIME, THE SKIN OF AGHASURA BECAME STIFF AND DRY AND IT BECAME A FAVOURITE PLACE FOR THE CHILDREN TO PLAY.

"WHEN KRISHNA AND BALARAMA WERE SIX, THEY WERE ALLOWED TO GO FURTHER FROM HOME, INTO THE DEEP FOREST WITH THEIR COWS.

"THE SCENTED FLOWERS, THE SPARKLING WATERS OF THE BEAUTIFUL LAKES, THE GALLOPING DEER AND THE SWEET SOUND OF BIRDSONG IN THE FORESTS OF VRINDAVAN NEVER FAILED TO DELIGHT KRISHNA. ONE DAY KRISHNA AND BALARAMA WERE RESTING AFTER PLAY,

"AMONG THEIR COWHERD FRIENDS WERE SUBALA AND SHRIDAMA. THEY SAID —

YOU, BALARAMA AND KRISHNA, ARE UNEQUALLED IN STRENGTH. DO YOU KNOW THERE IS A DENSE FOREST NEAR BY WITH SEVERAL PALM TREES LADEN WITH FRUIT?

"SHRIDAMA SAID —

BUT THERE IS A WICKED ASURA NAMED DHENUKA LIVING THERE IN THE GUISE OF A DONKEY. HE DOES NOT ALLOW ANYONE, NEITHER MAN NOR BEAST, TO ENCROACH UPON THAT AREA. DESPITE THE LURE OF THE FRUIT, NO ONE DARES TO GO INTO THAT FOREST.

BUT YOU MUST HELP US GET THAT FRUIT, KRISHNA.

"WITH A LAUGH, KRISHNA AND BALARAMA SPRANG UP.

COME, SHOW US THE WAY.

YES, LET'S GO RIGHT NOW.

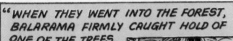

"WHEN THEY WENT INTO THE FOREST, BALARAMA FIRMLY CAUGHT HOLD OF ONE OF THE TREES.

"... AND SHOOK IT SO VIGOROUSLY THAT MANY FRUIT FELL DOWN. THE ASURA CAME RUNNING AS HE HEARD THE SOUND.

"WITH HIS HIND LEGS, HE GAVE A SWIFT KICK TO BALARAMA.

"BUT WHEN HE TRIED TO DO SO AGAIN, BALARAMA CAUGHT HOLD OF HIS LEGS...

"... AND TWIRLED HIM ROUND SO FAST THAT THE ASURA DIED.

" BALARAMA THEN FLUNG DHENUKASURA UP AND HE FELL ON THE TOP OF A PALM TREE.

" WITH A LOUD NOISE, THE TREE CRASHED TO THE GROUND, FELLING A NUMBER OF OTHER TREES TOO.

" KRISHNA AND BALARAMA RETURNED HOME HAPPY. FROM THAT DAY ON, PEOPLE OF VRINDAVAN VENTURED FEARLESSLY INTO THE FOREST TO EAT THE PALM FRUIT AND GRAZE THEIR CATTLE.

" BALARAMA AND KRISHNA WERE USUALLY INSEPARABLE. ONE DAY, HOWEVER, KRISHNA WENT WITH HIS OTHER FRIENDS TO THE BANKS OF THE YAMUNA, LEAVING BALARAMA BEHIND.

"IT WAS A HOT, DRY SUMMER'S DAY AND THE COWHERDS WERE THIRSTY.

DON'T DRINK THE WATER FROM THAT POOL. IT IS POISONED.

YES, THAT SERPENT KALIYA LIVES INSIDE.

HIS VENOM IS SO POWERFUL THAT EVEN THE PLANTS NEAR THE POND HAVE WILTED.

BUT OUR COWS ARE SO THIRSTY!

"UNMINDFUL OF THE WARNING, THE COWHERDS LED THE CATTLE TO THE RIVER.

"NO SOONER HAD THEY DRUNK THE WATER THAN THE CATTLE COLLAPSED ON THE RIVER BANK.

"KRISHNA COULD NOT BEAR TO SEE THIS.

"SWIFTLY, HE CLAMBERED UP A TREE...

KRISHNA! WHAT ARE YOU DOING?

"...AND DIVED INTO THE POND.

"PLAYFULLY HE BEGAN TO SPLASH ABOUT IN THE WATER. KALIYA, THE SERPENT, HEARD THE SOUND.

"...AND SUDDENLY EMERGING FROM THE DEPTHS, APPEARED BEFORE KRISHNA. WITH A HUNDRED AND ONE FORKED TONGUES LASHING OUT OF HIS HUNDRED AND ONE HEADS, HE WAS AN AWESOME SIGHT INDEED.

"BUT KRISHNA REMAINED CALM AND GAZED AT HIM WITH A GENTLE SMILE ON HIS LIPS.

"THIS MADE KALIYA ALL THE MORE ANGRY. HE POUNCED ON KRISHNA...

"...AND CAUGHT THE BOY IN HIS COILS.

"BY NOW THE COWHERD BOYS BECAME ALARMED.

KRISHNA IS CAUGHT! KRISHNA IS CAUGHT!

CALL NANDA.

SAVE HIM! HELP!

"ON HEARING THE NEWS, NANDA AND OTHERS RUSHED TO THE SPOT. SOME OF THE COWHERDS HAD FAINTED OUT OF FRIGHT.

"YASHODA WAS ABOUT TO JUMP INTO THE RIVER, BUT THE GOPIKAS HELD HER BACK FORCIBLY.

OH MY SON!

"THEY TRIED TO CONSOLE HER.

DON'T WORRY ABOUT KRISHNA.

REMEMBER HOW BRAVELY KRISHNA FACED THE WICKED POOTANA?

"BALARAMA COAXED NANDA AGAINST THE IDEA OF TRYING TO RESCUE KRISHNA.

"BOUND AS HE WAS IN THE SERPENT'S COILS, KRISHNA NOW MADE HIS BODY SWELL. HE GREW BIGGER...

"...AND BIGGER...

"...TILL HE GOT FREE FROM KALIYA'S HOLD. KALIYA BROKE AWAY, BUT RAISED HIS HOODS OMINOUSLY OVER KRISHNA.

"HE BLEW OUT SPRAYS OF VENOM THROUGH HIS NOSTRILS. HIS RED EYES GLARED AT KRISHNA. FLAMES SHOT OUT OF HIS MANY MOUTHS.

"KRISHNA PLAYFULLY DODGED EVERY ATTACK OF THE SERPENT.

"WHEN KALIYA SEEMED TO HAVE TIRED A LITTLE, IN ONE SWIFT LEAP KRISHNA WAS ON HIS HOOD.

"WITH RHYTHMIC STEPS, KRISHNA BEGAN TO DANCE ON KALIYA, NIMBLY STEPPING FROM ONE HEAD TO ANOTHER.

"AT THE TOUCH OF KRISHNA'S FEET, THE HEADS WERE CRUSHED. KALIYA SOON LOST HIS STRENGTH.

"BLOOD OOZED FROM HIS MOUTHS AND NOSTRILS, AND HE FELL IN A FAINT.

"REGAINING A LITTLE STRENGTH, KALIYA WOULD TRY TO LIFT ONE OF HIS HEADS.

"QUICKLY KRISHNA WOULD JUMP ON IT.

PAREEKSHIT INTERRUPTED SHUKADEVA IN HIS NARRATION.

DID KRISHNA KILL KALIYA?

KALIYA'S END SEEMED TO BE NEAR. JUST THEN, HIS WIVES AND CHILDREN, WHO WERE ALSO LIVING IN THAT POND, APPEARED BEFORE KRISHNA, AND BEGGED HIM TO LET KALIYA GO. THEIR ENTREATIES MOVED KRISHNA'S TENDER HEART, AND HE DECIDED TO SPARE KALIYA HIS LIFE.

"ADDRESSING KALIYA, KRISHNA SAID—

YOU MUST NOT STAY ANY LONGER IN THIS POOL. TAKE AWAY ALL YOUR KIN AND DEPART FOR THE HIGH SEAS.

"AS COMMANDED BY KRISHNA, KALIYA LEFT THE POOL AND WENT AWAY. THE WATER OF THE POOL BECAME MIRACULOUSLY PURE AND CLEAR.

"PEACE AND TRANQUILLITY RETURNED TO VRINDAVAN. EVEN IN THE HOT SUMMER DAYS, THE WEATHER REMAINED PLEASANT THERE, SURROUNDED AS THE PLACE WAS WITH DENSE FORESTS AND SPARKLING STREAMS. KRISHNA, BALARAMA AND THEIR FRIENDS REVELLED IN THE BEAUTIFUL SURROUNDINGS, WRESTLING IN THE LUSH GRASS, DANCING AND PLAYING HIDE AND SEEK.

"ONE DAY WHEN KRISHNA AND BALARAMA WERE TAKING THEIR CATTLE TO GRAZE BY THE RIVER-SIDE, PRALAMBA, THE ASURA, CAME THERE IN THE GUISE OF A COWHERD.

" KRISHNA HOWEVER WAS NOT FOOLED.

THERE IS SOMETHING ODD ABOUT THIS NEW BOY! I WILL HAVE TO TRICK HIM AND FIND OUT.

"HE CALLED ALL THE BOYS.

COME! WE WILL PLAY A NEW GAME TODAY.

WE WILL SPLIT INTO TWO TEAMS. WHO WILL BE THE LEADERS?

YOU AND BALARAMA, OF COURSE.

" KRISHNA AND BALARAMA CHOSE THEIR TEAMS AND PLAYED SEVERAL GAMES.

WE WON! OUR TEAM HAS WON THIS GAME. NOW FOR THE NEXT GAME, YOUR TEAM MUST CARRY OUR BOYS ON THEIR BACKS UP TO THAT TREE THERE.

" THE COWHERDS WERE THRILLED WITH THE NEW GAME. THE WINNER WOULD GLEEFULLY CLAMBER ONTO THE BACK OF THE LOSER.

"IN THE NEXT ROUND, PRALAMBA THE ASURA CARRIED BALARAMA.

KRISHNA IS TOO STRONG FOR ME. I WILL NOT BE ABLE TO DEFEAT HIM. LET ME TAKE THIS CHANCE AND CARRY BALARAMA AT LEAST.

"SO PRALAMBA HURRIED TO THE TARGET TREE. BUT INSTEAD OF STOPPING THERE, HE RAN FURTHER...

"...AND FURTHER. BUT SOON HE FELT FATIGUED WITH THE WEIGHT OF BALARAMA.

OHH! THIS LITTLE BOY IS TOO HEAVY. I C-A-N-T CARRY HIM FURTHER.

"WHEN HE PAUSED FOR BREATH, PANTING AND SWEATING, HE ASSUMED HIS ASURA FORM.

"THE FAIR FORM OF BALARAMA SHONE RADIANTLY ATOP THE DARK BODY OF PRALAMBA, LIKE THE RESPLENDENT MOON IN A DARK CLOUD.

"NOW THE ASURA BEGAN TO FLY UPWARDS.

WHAT'S THIS? I AM BEING CARRIED UP BY THIS UGLY CREATURE.

TAKE THIS!

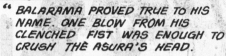

"BALARAMA PROVED TRUE TO HIS NAME. ONE BLOW FROM HIS CLENCHED FIST WAS ENOUGH TO CRUSH THE ASURA'S HEAD.

"DOWN HE COLLAPSED TO THE EARTH, IN A HEAP.

AHHH!

"THE ANXIOUS COWHERDS WHO HAD BY NOW FOLLOWED THE PAIR, WERE RELIEVED TO SEE BALARAMA SAFE AND SOUND.

BRAVO, BALARAMA!

WELL DONE!

YOU WERE REALLY COURAGEOUS BALARAMA!

"CHILDREN THAT THEY WERE, THE COWHERDS, ALONG WITH KRISHNA AND BALARAMA, SOON WENT BACK TO THEIR FUN AND FROLIC.

LET'S PLAY HIDE AND SEEK NOW!

"MEANWHILE THEIR COWS WANDERED OFF...

"...AND STRAYED INTO A DENSE WOOD NEAR BY, IN SEARCH OF TENDER GREEN GRASS.

"AFTER A WHILE, THE BOYS NOTICED THEIR ABSENCE.

WHERE ARE THE COWS? I CAN'T HEAR THEM LOWING.

THEY MUST HAVE WANDERED OFF.

LET'S LOOK FOR THEM. HERE ARE SOME TRACKS!

"BUT THOUGH THEY LOOKED FOR LONG —

OH DEAR! I HOPE WE FIND THEM.

WE CANNOT GO BACK WITHOUT THEM. AND IT IS GETTING QUITE LATE.

HERE ARE SOME MORE TRACKS.

THERE! I CAN SEE THEM NOW. IN THAT THICKET THERE.

"BY THE TIME THEY ROUNDED UP ALL THEIR CATTLE, THE BOYS WERE EXTREMELY TIRED.

COME RAMBHA! COME! THERE, ALL OF THEM ARE TOGETHER NOW.

"JUST THEN, A FOREST FIRE BROKE OUT.

"WHIPPED BY A STRONG WIND, THE FLAMES SPREAD RAPIDLY. THE COWHERDS AND CATTLE FOUND THEMSELVES IN THE MIDST OF A RAGING FIRE.

HELP! KRISHNA, BALARAMA.

PROTECT US, KRISHNA!

"HEARING THE CRIES OF HIS COMPANIONS, KRISHNA SAID

DON'T BE AFRAID. JUST CLOSE YOUR EYES.

AS YOU SAY.

"KRISHNA THEN OPENED HIS MOUTH WIDE, AND THE LEAPING FLAMES WERE DRAWN INTO HIS MOUTH.

SHUKADEVA TOLD PAREEKSHIT ABOUT THE MIRACLE PERFORMED BY KRISHNA.

O PAREEKSHIT, LORD KRISHNA SWALLOWED THE FIRE. WHEN THE COWHERDS OPENED THEIR EYES, THEY FOUND THEMSELVES IN THE SHADE OF THE TREE WHERE THEY HAD BEEN PLAYING EARLIER IN THE DAY.

"AT THE END OF THIS LONG AND EVENTFUL DAY, KRISHNA AND BALARAMA LED THEIR FRIENDS BACK HOME, CHEERFULLY PLAYING THEIR FLUTES.

THUS ENDS THE SECOND SESSION OF OUR RENDERING OF THE TENTH CHAPTER OF THE BHAGAWAT PURANA.

AMAR CHITRA KATHA

KRISHNA—THE UPHOLDER OF GOVARDHANA

SHUKADEVA, WHO WAS NARRATING THE STORY OF KRISHNA TO PAREEKSHIT, SAID—

WHEN THE COWHERD BOYS RETURNED HOME AND RELATED THE EXPLOITS OF KRISHNA AND BALARAMA TO THE PEOPLE OF VRINDAVANA, THEY WERE STRUCK WITH WONDER. THEY BEGAN TO BELIEVE THAT TWO DIVINE BEINGS HAD BEEN BORN IN THEIR MIDST.

"THEN THE RAINY SEASON SET IN. THE EARTH, SCORCHED BY THE SUMMER HEAT, WAS BLANKETED WITH LUSH GREEN GRASS.

"THE FOREST TREES, LADEN WITH BLACK-BERRIES, SEEMED TO BECKON KRISHNA AND HIS MATES.

"ON SOME DAYS THEY WOULD SIT ON A ROCK AND EAT THEIR FOOD, ENJOYING THE PITTER-PATTER OF THE RAIN.

"BUT WHEN THE SHOWERS BECAME HEAVY, THEY WOULD RUN TO THE SHELTER OF A CAVE, OR HIDE IN THE HOLLOW OF A TREE, TO ESCAPE THEIR FURY.

THE CLOUDS DISPERSED AND THE STORMY WINDS BECAME QUIET. NOW IT WAS AUTUMN. THE STARS SHONE BRIGHTLY IN THE CLOUDLESS SKIES.

"WHEN THE GOPIKAS OF VRINDAVANA HEARD THE SWEET SOUND OF KRISHNA'S MELODIOUS FLUTE THEY WOULD STOP ALL WORK AND LISTEN.

OH THAT KRISHNA! HOW ENCHANTING HE IS WITH THE PEACOCK FEATHER IN HIS CURLS, YELLOW FLOWERS IN HIS EARS, THE GOLDEN CLOTH DRAPED OVER HIS DARK FORM, AND THE GARLAND OF FRAGRANT FLOWERS AROUND HIS NECK.

WHEN HE PLAYS HIS FLUTE, EVEN THE BEASTS OF THE JUNGLE STOP TO HEAR HIM.

WHY TALK OF THE BIRDS AND THE BEASTS. EVEN THE STREAMS AND RIVERS SEEM TO RESPOND TO THE MELODY OF KRISHNA'S FLUTE.

LEAVE ALONE THE EARTH, EVEN THE CLOUDS IN THE SKY SEEM TO BE EAGER TO PROTECT KRISHNA. THE TINY RAIN DROPS ARE LIKE LITTLE WHITE FLOWER OFFERINGS MADE TO OUR KRISHNA.

"WHEN WINTER SET IN, THE MAIDENS OF VRAJA OBSERVED THEIR CUSTOMARY PRAYERS TO THE GODDESS DURGA.

"SINGING AND CHATTING, THEY WOULD GO TOGETHER TO BATHE IN THE YAMUNA AT DAY-BREAK, MAKE A CLAY IMAGE OF THE GODDESS ON THE BANK, AND PRAY TO IT.

"ONE DAY, THEY WERE SPLASHING ABOUT IN THE WATER.

LOOK, OUR CLOTHES HAVE VANISHED.

STRANGE. WE HAD LEFT THEM ON THE BANK THERE.

"JUST THEN THEY SAW KRISHNA SITTING ASTRIDE THE BRANCH OF A KADAMBA TREE NEAR BY.

HA! HA! HA!

COME AND COLLECT YOUR BELONGINGS.

THAT'S NOT FAIR, KRISHNA. DON'T TORMENT US SO.

COME, KRISHNA, WE KNOW YOU ARE NANDA'S DARLING SON. ALL THE PEOPLE OF VRAJA DOTE ON YOU. WE TOO ARE EVER WILLING TO DO YOUR BIDDING.

IN THAT CASE, YOU MUST COME HERE, BOW TO ME, AND TAKE YOUR BELONGINGS.

SHUKADEVA SAID TO PAREEKSHIT —

KRISHNA WAS TRYING TO TEST THE DEVOTION OF THE GOPIKAS FOR HIM. HE TEASED AND TAUNTED THEM, LAUGHED AT THEIR PLIGHT, MADE THEM ACT LIKE PUPPETS AT HIS MERCY. YET THEY WERE NOT ANNOYED WITH HIM.

"AFTER THEY HAD COLLECTED THEIR CLOTHES FROM KRISHNA, HE SAID —

MAY YOUR DESIRES BE ALL FULFILLED. NOW RETURN TO YOUR HOMES, DEAR MAIDENS, AND AWAIT THE MOONLIT NIGHTS OF AUTUMN.

"ONE DAY WHEN KRISHNA AND THE COWHERDS WERE GRAZING THEIR COWS, HE SAID —

BEHOLD THESE TREES. THEY BEAR THE SEVERE SUN, THE LASHING WIND AND RAIN, AND YET PROTECT US. LEAVES AND FLOWERS, BARK AND WOOD, SAP AND GUM, FUEL AND FRUITS. MANY ARE THE GIFTS THE TREES BESTOW ON US. BLESSED ARE THE PEOPLE WHO GIVE GENEROUSLY TO OTHERS LIKE THESE TREES.

"HUNGRY AND THIRSTY, THE BOYS APPROACHED THE RIVER BANK.

KRISHNA, WE HAVE QUENCHED OUR THIRST WITH THE RIVER WATER. BUT I AM FEELING VERY HUNGRY.

ME TOO. KRISHNA, BALARAMA, YOU MUST THINK OF A WAY TO SATISFY OUR HUNGER.

"KRISHNA SAID —

A LITTLE DISTANCE FROM HERE, THERE IS A GROUP OF BRAHMANAS PERFORMING A YAJNA. TELL THEM THAT KRISHNA AND BALARAMA HAVE SENT YOU, AND THEY WILL SURELY GIVE YOU SOME FOOD.

WE'VE BEEN SENT BY KRISHNA AND BALARAMA. DO GIVE US SOME FOOD, O BRAHMANAS!

"BUT THE BRAHMANAS IGNORED THE BOYS AND CONTINUED THEIR YAJNA.

"SADLY, THE COWHERD BOYS RETURNED TO KRISHNA.

WHAT HAPPENED? DIDN'T THE BRAHMANAS GIVE YOU ANY FOOD?

THEY SAID NEITHER YES NOR NO. WE FELT DISAPPOINTED.

"KRISHNA SAID WITH A LAUGH —

JUST BECAUSE YOU ARE UNSUCCESSFUL ONCE, YOU MUST NOT STOP TRYING. GO AND MEET THEIR WIVES THIS TIME. THEY ARE DEVOTED TO ME AND WILL CERTAINLY GIVE YOU FOOD.

"OBEDIENTLY THE COWHERDS WENT BACK AND REQUESTED THE WIVES OF THE BRAHMANAS.

KRISHNA AND BALARAMA HAVE SENT US TO YOU. THEY ARE HUNGRY AND HAVE REQUESTED YOU FOR SOME FOOD.

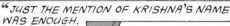

"JUST THE MENTION OF KRISHNA'S NAME WAS ENOUGH.

FOR KRISHNA! SURELY WE WILL DO ANYTHING TO HAVE A GLIMPSE OF HIM.

FOR SO LONG WE HAVE HEARD OF HIS PRAISE. THOUGH WE HAVE NEVER SEEN HIM, HE HAS BECOME VERY DEAR TO US.

"LIKE RIVERS RUSHING TO MEET THE SEA, THE WOMEN EAGERLY HURRIED TO MEET KRISHNA. THEY CARRIED VESSELS FILLED WITH DELICIOUS FOOD THEY HAD COOKED FOR THE YAJNA BEING PERFORMED BY THEIR HUSBANDS.

"WHEN THEY BEHELD KRISHNA, SHINING BRIGHTLY IN HIS BEAUTIFUL GOLDEN GARMENTS, THE CURLY LOCKS AROUND HIS SMILING, DUSKY FACE, THEY WERE DELIGHTED AT THE SIGHT.

"WITH A PLAYFUL SMILE, KRISHNA SAID—

WELCOME, DEAR LADIES. I KNOW YOUR DEVOTION FOR ME HAS DRAWN YOU HERE. YOUR LOVE FOR ME IS INDEED PURE AND SELFLESS.

BUT NOW THAT YOU HAVE MET ME, YOU MUST RETURN TO YOUR HOMES. YOUR PRESENCE IS NECESSARY TO COMPLETE THE YAJNA BEING PERFORMED BY YOUR HUSBANDS.

"THE WOMEN REPLIED—

DON'T SEND US AWAY. WE HAVE COME TO YOU, ABANDONING EVERYTHING. OUR FAMILIES MAY NOT ACCEPT US NOW. YOU ARE OUR ONLY HOPE.

"KRISHNA GENTLY REASSURED THEM.

REST ASSURED, NO ONE WILL TALK ILL OF YOU. EVEN THE CELESTIALS WILL ADMIRE YOUR DEVOTION. YOU MAY KEEP ME IN YOUR MIND, BUT GO BACK NOW.

"INDEED WHEN THEIR WIVES RETURNED TO THE SACRIFICIAL HALL, THE BRAHMANAS ACCEPTED THEIR RETURN WITHOUT ANY COMMENT AND PROCEEDED TO COMPLETE THE YAJNA.

"WHILE KRISHNA AND HIS COMPANIONS HAPPILY FEASTED ON THE FOOD BROUGHT BY THE WIVES OF THE BRAHMANAS...

"... THE BRAHMANAS, WHO HAD IGNORED KRISHNA'S REQUEST, WERE FILLED WITH REMORSE.

FIE ON US! WE IGNORED THE REQUEST OF LORD KRISHNA HIMSELF. OF WHAT USE IS OUR KNOWLEDGE?

AND LOOK AT THE DEVOTION OF OUR WIVES FOR THE LORD. THESE WOMEN HAVE NEITHER LEARNT THE VEDAS NOR UNDERGONE PENANCE. YET THEY HAVE UTTER FAITH IN LORD KRISHNA. HOW LUCKY WE ARE TO HAVE SUCH WIVES.

"OVERCOME WITH SHAME AND REPENTANCE, THE BRAHMANAS LONGED TO MEET KRISHNA AND BALARAMA. BUT FEAR OF KAMSA HELD THEM BACK.

"IN VRINDAVANA, KRISHNA NOTICED ALL THE COWHERDS WERE BUSY PREPARING FOR SOME YAJNA. APPROACHING HIS FATHER, HE ASKED —

FATHER, WHAT CELEBRATION ARE YOU ALL BUSY PREPARING FOR?

WHAT IS THE MERIT OF THIS YAJNA? WHAT IS ITS PURPOSE? WHO ARE THE PEOPLE WHO WILL PERFORM IT? DO TELL ME, FATHER.

"NANDA SAID —

LORD INDRA IS THE GOD OF THE RAIN CLOUDS. HE IS THE ONE WHO SHOWERS THE LIFE-GIVING RAIN ON US. WE PERFORM YAJNAS TO PLEASE HIM.

WHY, EVEN THE MATERIALS USED FOR THE YAJNA ARE PRODUCED BECAUSE OF THE RAIN. FOR SEVERAL GENERATIONS WE HAVE BEEN VENERATING INDRA THUS.

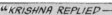

"KRISHNA REPLIED —

A LIVING BEING IS BORN AND DIES ACCORDING TO HIS KARMA. JOY AND SORROW, FEAR AND PROSPERITY ARE ALL AN OUTCOME OF KARMA. WHY THEN DO WE NEED INDRA?

A MAN SHOULD WORSHIP WHATEVER HE LIVES BY. FOR VAISHYAS LIKE US, FOUR TYPES OF LIVELIHOOD ARE POSSIBLE — AGRI- CULTURE, TRADE, CATTLE- REARING AND MONEY-LENDING.

WE ARE FOREST DWELLERS. FOR LONG, OUR PEOPLE HAVE TENDED CATTLE. THESE FORESTS AND MOUNTAINS ARE OUR HOMES. LET US THEREFORE WORSHIP OUR COWS, AND OUR MOUNTAINS.

ALL THESE THINGS THAT HAVE BEEN COLLECTED FOR INDRA'S YAJNA, LET THEM BE USED FOR THE OTHER SACRIFICE.

SUMMON WELL-VERSED BRAHMANAS TO CONDUCT THE SACRIFICE. LET A SUMPTUOUS FEAST BE PREPARED. WE WILL MAKE AN OFFERING TO THIS MOUNTAIN HERE.

THEN BEDECKING OURSELVES IN FINE GARMENTS AND JEWELS, WE WILL GO ROUND THE COWS, THE BRAHMANAS AND MOUNT GOVARDHANA. THIS IS MY OPINION, FATHER. SUCH A SACRIFICE WILL PLEASE ME IMMENSELY.

NANDA AND THE OTHER COWHERDS WERE CONVINCED.

WE WILL DO AS YOU SAY, KRISHNA.

YES, LET'S START THE PREPARATIONS.

BRAHMANAS LIGHTED THE HOLY FIRE AND RECITED THE SACRED MANTRAS.

THE COWHERDS PRESENTED THE BRAHMANAS WITH GIFTS.

THE COWS WERE OFFERED TENDER LUSH GLASS. VARIOUS OFFERINGS WERE ALSO PLACED BEFORE MOUNT GOVARDHANA.

WITH NANDA LEADING THE WAY, THE COWHERDS WENT ROUND GOVARDHANA.

THE GAILY DRESSED GOPIKAS SAT ON BULLOCK-CARTS AND WENT ROUND THE MOUNTAIN WHILE SINGING SONGS IN PRAISE OF KRISHNA.

I MUST CONVINCE THEM THAT THEIR ACTION IS RIGHT. LET ME ASSUME ANOTHER FORM.

"KRISHNA APPEARED IN THE GUISE OF AN ENORMOUS BEING ON THE TOP OF MOUNT GOVARDHANA.

I AM GOVARDHANA

"BEFORE THEIR VERY EYES, THE GIGANTIC FORM BEGAN TO GOBBLE UP THE OFFERINGS MADE TO IT. FEIGNING SURPRISE, KRISHNA SAID —

HOW WONDERFUL! BEHOLD HOW THE MOUNTAIN HAS GRACED US WITH HIS PRESENCE.

HE CAN ASSUME ANY FORM. HE CAN DESTROY ANY ONE WHO DISRESPECTS HIM. FOR THE WELFARE OF OUR CATTLE AND OURSELVES, LET US BOW BEFORE HIM.

"THUS INSPIRED BY KRISHNA, ALL THE PEOPLE OF VRINDAVANA WORSHIPPED THE MOUNTAIN, THE COWS AND BRAHMANAS, AND RETURNED TO THEIR HOMES.

"NOW THAT HIS WORSHIP HAD BEEN DISCONTINUED, INDRA WAS VERY ANGRY.

HOW DARE THEY DO THIS TO ME, THE LORD OF THE THREE WORLDS!

"HE SUMMONED THE DESTRUCTIVE MASSES OF CLOUDS CALLED SAMVARTAKA.

BEHOLD THE ARROGANCE OF THESE COWHERDS. THEY ARE INTOXICATED WITH THEIR WEALTH.

ON THE WORD OF KRISHNA, THE PEOPLE OF VRAJA HAVE INSULTED ME AND FAILED TO PAY ME HOMAGE.

THAT IGNORANT, VAIN AND TALKATIVE KRISHNA THINKS HE IS VERY WISE. HE HAS ENCOURAGED THE PEOPLE OF VRINDA-VANA TO DEFY ME. I COMMAND YOU TO DESTROY THEIR VANITY.

ATTACK THEM! KILL THEIR CATTLE! I WILL FOLLOW YOU WITH MY ARMY OF ELEPHANTS, WITH AIRAVATA LEADING THE WAY.

"WITH THESE WORDS, INDRA RELEASED THE CLOUDS.

"HASTILY THEY SPED TOWARDS VRAJA AND INUNDATED VRAJA WITH A HEAVY DOWNPOUR.

"LIGHTNING APPEARED IN AWESOME STREAKS WITH CRASHES OF THUNDER. A MIGHTY GALE BLEW ACROSS THE LAND, HURLING HAILSTONES IN ITS WAKE. HUGE COLUMNS OF WATER RAINED DOWN ON VRAJA, FLOODING IT COMPLETELY.

"FRIGHTENED BY THE DELUGE, SHIVERING AND DRENCHED BY THE RAIN, THE GOPAS AND GOPIKAS RAN TO KRISHNA FOR HELP.

KRISHNA! DEAR KRISHNA! YOU ARE OUR ONLY HOPE NOW. SAVE US FROM INDRA'S WRATH.

"SEEING THEIR PLIGHT, KRISHNA THOUGHT—

SURELY, INDRA HAS CAUSED THIS UN-SEASONAL, HEAVY RAIN AND HAILSTORM BECAUSE WE DID NOT WORSHIP HIM.

BUT I WILL GIVE HIM A FITTING REPLY. THIS BEHAVIOUR DOESN'T BEFIT A DEVA LIKE HIM. I MUST CRUSH HIS PRIDE FOR HIS OWN GOOD. I MUST SAVE MY PEOPLE.

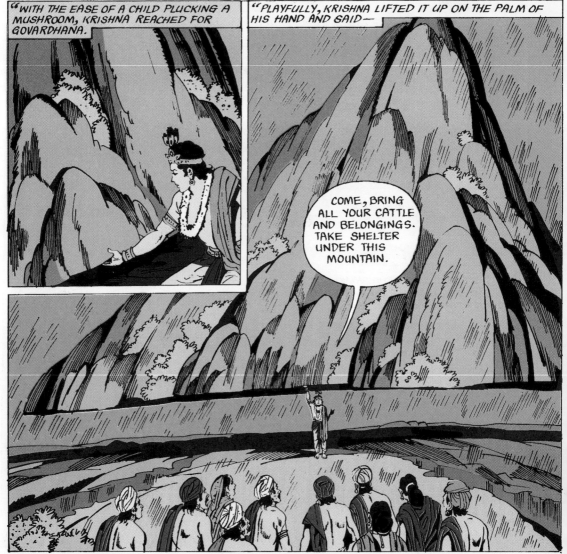

"WITH THE EASE OF A CHILD PLUCKING A MUSHROOM, KRISHNA REACHED FOR GOVARDHANA.

"PLAYFULLY, KRISHNA LIFTED IT UP ON THE PALM OF HIS HAND AND SAID—

COME, BRING ALL YOUR CATTLE AND BELONGINGS. TAKE SHELTER UNDER THIS MOUNTAIN.

REST ASSURED. GOVARDHANA WILL NOT FALL FROM MY HANDS. I HAVE DONE THIS TO PROTECT YOU FROM THE RAIN AND STORM.

"THUS REASSURED, THE PEOPLE OF VRAJA HURRIEDLY GATHERED THEIR CATTLE, CARTS AND OTHER BELONGINGS, AND TOOK SHELTER UNDER THE MOUNTAIN.

"FOR SEVEN LONG DAYS AND NIGHTS KRISHNA CARRIED ALOFT THE MOUNT GOVARDHANA, WITHOUT HAVING FOOD AND DRINK.

"INDRA WAS AMAZED TO SEE KRISHNA'S FEAT.

"ALL HIS PRIDE VANISHED. HE BADE THE CLOUDS TO STOP THEIR DOWNPOUR.

"KRISHNA SAW THAT THE RAIN AND THUNDER HAD STOPPED AND THE SUN WAS SHINING AGAIN.

GO OUT, MY DEAR FOLKS! THE STORM HAS BLOWN OVER, THE FLOOD WATER TOO HAS RECEDED.

"SLOWLY, PEOPLE BEGAN TO EMERGE WITH THEIR BELONGINGS.

"WHEN THE LAST PERSON WAS SAFELY OUT, KRISHNA CAREFULLY PUT THE MOUNTAIN BACK IN ITS PLACE.

"FILLED WITH GRATITUDE AND AFFECTION, THE PEOPLE OF VRAJA RUSHED TO THANK KRISHNA.

"YASHODA, ROHINI AND NANDA HUGGED KRISHNA.

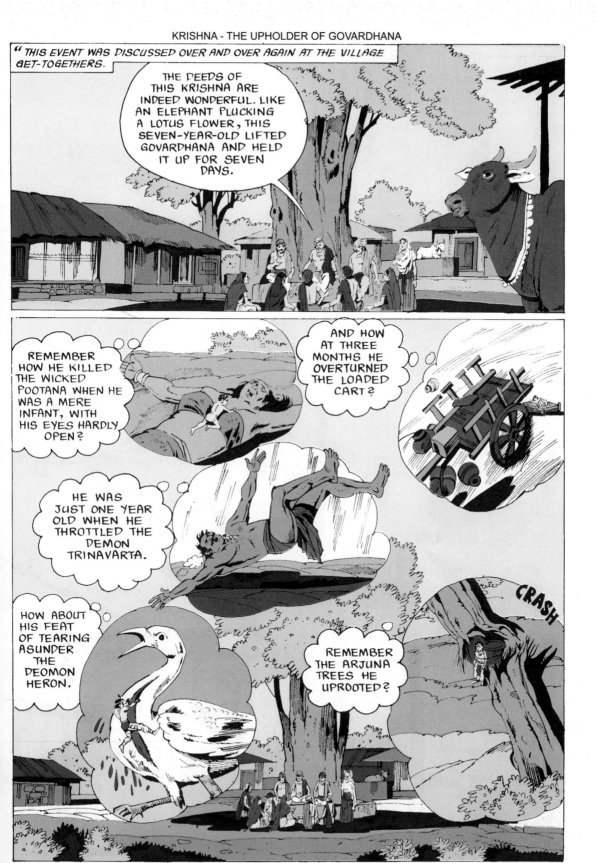

IS IT NOT A WONDER THAT AN EXTRAORDINARY BOY LIKE HIM HAS BEEN BORN IN OUR MIDST?

TELL US, NANDA, WHY IS IT THAT YOUR DUSKY BOY IS SUCH A FAVOURITE OF THE ENTIRE VILLAGE?

YES, NANDA, WE ARE BEGINNING TO BE SUSPICIOUS ABOUT YOUR SON.

"NANDA REPLIED —

HEAR ME WELL. I WILL REMOVE ALL YOUR DOUBTS. GARGACHARYA HAS TOLD ME THAT THIS BOY OF MINE HAS NUMEROUS NAMES AND FORMS.

THIS BOY WILL BRING GOOD FORTUNE TO YOU AND YOUR PEOPLE. IN BEAUTY, FAME AND GLORY, YOUR SON IS EQUAL TO VISHNU. SO DON'T BE AMAZED AT HIS EXTRA-ORDINARY DEEDS.

SINCE THAT DAY, I CONSIDER THIS BOY AS A PART OF VISHNU.

NOW WE UNDERSTAND!

NO WONDER HE IS SO POWERFUL.

"SOME DAYS LATER, WHEN NANDA OBSERVED THE EKADASHI* FAST, AFTER PRAYING ALL DAY, HE STEPPED INTO THE WATER OF YAMUNA FOR A BATH IN THE EVENING.

"THE TIME BETWEEN SUNDOWN AND DAY-BREAK WAS CONSIDERED INAUSPICIOUS SINCE THE DEMONS WERE AT LARGE THEN. ONE OF THEM CAUGHT HOLD OF NANDA AND DRAGGED HIM AWAY.

"WHEN THE COWHERDS SAW HIM DISAPPEAR UNDERWATER, THEY CRIED OUT.

KRISHNA! KRISHNA! RESCUE YOUR FATHER.

HURRY, BALARAMA HURRY!

"HEARING THEIR CRIES, KRISHNA RUSHED TO THE SPOT AND DIVED INTO THE WATER TO CONFRONT VARUNA, THE LORD OF THE NETHER WORLD.

* 11TH DAY OF THE LUNAR CALENDAR.

"FILLED WITH AWE AND JOY AT THE SIGHT OF KRISHNA, VARUNA BOWED DOWN TO WORSHIP HIM.

ACCEPT MY PRAYERS, O LORD. FORGIVE MY SERVANT FOR SEIZING YOUR FATHER. YOU ARE A WITNESS TO ALL OUR ACTION.

"NANDA WAS AMAZED TO SEE THE WEALTH AND RICHES OF VARUNA AND THE SPLENDOUR OF HIS PALACE. BUT MORE SO BY HIS ATTITUDE TOWARDS KRISHNA.

HOW RESPECTFULLY AND HUMBLY VARUNA APPROACHES KRISHNA.

"WHEN KRISHNA RETURNED WITH NANDA TO VRAJA, HE RELATED THE EVENTS TO HIS FRIENDS.

...AND THEN VARUNA HIMSELF BOWED TO MY KRISHNA.

WHY, HE IS THE LORD HIMSELF.

WILL HE EVER REVEAL TO US HIS TRUE SELF?

"KRISHNA LEARNT WHAT WAS IN THEIR MINDS, AND SOON REVEALED TO THEM HIS INFINITE FORM. THEY WERE FILLED WITH ECSTASY AT THE SIGHT.

"ON A FULL MOON NIGHT IN AUTUMN, KRISHNA PLAYED AN ENCHANTING TUNE ON HIS FLUTE.

"IN THE STILL OF THE NIGHT, THE LILTING MELODY REACHED THE EARS OF THE GOPIKAS.

"CASTING ASIDE THEIR PATIENCE, FEAR, AND EMBARRASSMENT, THE GOPIKAS RAN OUT OF THEIR HOMES.

"DRAWN BY THE SPELL OF KRISHNA'S FLUTE, THEY HURRIED TO THE RIVER BANK, THEIR LONG EARRINGS DANGLING AS IF KEEPING RHYTHM WITH THEIR PACE.

"EVEN THE GOPIKAS WHO WERE IN THE MIDST OF THEIR HOUSEHOLD CHORES LEFT THEIR WORK UNFINISHED AND RAN OUT.

"ONE LEFT HOME AS THE MILK WAS BOILING ON THE FIRE.

"ANOTHER WHO WAS ADORNING HERSELF RUSHED OUT WITH HER TRESSES FLYING AND KAJAL* SMEARED.

"EVEN WHEN THE ELDERS IN THEIR FAMILIES TRIED TO RESTRAIN THEM, THEY PAID NO HEED, AND RAN OUT.

"THOSE WHO WERE FORCEFULLY CONFINED AT HOME, CLOSED THEIR EYES AND MEDITATED ON KRISHNA AND FELT A DEEP SENSE OF BLISS.

PAREEKSHIT INTERRUPTED THE NARRATION—

BUT THE DEVOTION OF THE GOPIKAS WAS NOT DIVINE; IT WAS EARTHLY LOVE.

SHUKADEVA REPLIED—

ALL THAT IS NEEDED IS TO REACH OUT FOR THE LORD—BE IT THROUGH DESIRE, ANGER OR FEAR. WHETHER IT IS A BOND OF AFFECTION, REVERENCE OR FRIENDSHIP, IT WILL BRING YOU CLOSE TO HIM.

"WHEN KRISHNA SAW THE GOPIKAS GATHERED AROUND HIM, HE SAID WITH A DISARMING SMILE—

WELCOME! WHAT BRINGS YOU HERE AT THIS TIME OF THE NIGHT? WHAT CAN I DO TO PLEASE YOU?

* COLLYRIUM

THE FOREST TREES, LADEN WITH FLOWERS, ARE INDEED ENCHANTING IN THE MELLOW LIGHT OF THE FULL MOON. THE COOL BREEZE, CARESSING THE WAVES, IS SOOTHING TOO. BUT DO NOT LINGER HERE. YOUR HUSBANDS AWAIT YOU. GO BACK TO YOUR HOMES.

"THE GOPIKAS WERE DISAPPOINTED WITH HIS WORDS. WITH THEIR HEADS CAST DOWN, THEY BIT THEIR LIPS TO CONTROL THEIR TEARS.

"IN VOICES CHOKED WITH EMOTION, THEY SAID TO KRISHNA—

ACCEPT OUR DEVOTION, O KRISHNA. IT IS NO LONGER A SECRET THAT YOU HAVE APPEARED IN VRAJA FOR OUR PRO-TECTION. ALLOW US TO SERVE YOU.

"WITH A SMILE, KRISHNA AGREED. ON THE WIDE EXPANSE OF SILVERY SANDS NEAR THE YAMUNA, KRISHNA BEGAN TO SPORT WITH THE GOPIKAS.

"SHINING BRIGHTLY, LIKE A MOON SUR-ROUNDED BY STARS, KRISHNA SANG AND DANCED WITH THE GOPIKAS.

"DELIGHTED WITH HIS ATTENTIONS, EACH GOPIKA THOUGHT HERSELF TO BE THE BEST WOMAN ON EARTH.

"NOTING THEIR PRIDE, KRISHNA SUDDENLY VANISHED FROM THEIR MIDST.

"WHEN THE GOPIKAS BECAME AWARE OF HIS ABSENCE, THEY WERE FILLED WITH DESPAIR AND ANXIETY.

WHERE IS KRISHNA?

WHY, HE WAS RIGHT HERE A MOMENT AGO!

"IN THEIR SEARCH FOR LORD KRISHNA, THEY EVEN TALKED TO THE TREES.

O PEEPUL! HAVE YOU SEEN THE SON OF NANDA, THE ONE WITH A LOVELY SMILE?

KACHNAR, CHAMPAK, JAMUN, KADAMBA*! TELL US WHERE TO FIND KRISHNA.

"THE GOPIKAS WERE SO ABSORBED IN KRISHNA THAT THEY MOMENTARILY FORGOT THEMSELVES, AND COMPLETELY IDENTIFIED WITH HIM.

I AM KRISHNA.

"ONE GOPIKA ENACTED THE LIFTING OF GOVARDHANA.

I AM KRISHNA. DON'T BE AFRAID OF THE RAIN. I'LL PROTECT YOU.

"ANOTHER PLAYED THE ROLE OF KRISHNA OVERPOWERING KALIYA.

O VILE SERPENT GO AWAY! DON'T YOU KNOW I HAVE TAKEN BIRTH TO PUNISH THE WICKED?

"ONE GOPIKA SAID—

I AM BABY KRISHNA, AND YOU ARE THE CART. I'LL CRY AND OVERTURN YOU WITH MY FEET.

"AS THEY WERE WANDERING IN THE FORESTS IN SEARCH OF KRISHNA—

WAIT! SEE THESE FOOTSTEPS.

YES, THEY ARE KRISHNA'S.

LET'S FOLLOW THEM.

BUT, LOOK, THERE IS ANOTHER TRACK BESIDE.

THEY ARE A GIRL'S.

LET'S GO AHEAD AND SEE WHO HIS FAVOURITE IS.

LOOK HERE! THE MARKS OF KRISHNA STANDING ON TIP-TOE. HE MUST HAVE BEEN PLUCKING FLOWERS FOR HER HERE.

"KRISHNA WANTED TO TEACH A LESSON TO THE PROUD WOMEN AND HAD INDEED GONE AWAY WITH ONE OF THEM.

"THE GOPIKA WHO HAD ACCOMPANIED KRISHNA, WAS ELATED.

I AM INDEED THE BEST. I AM KRISHNA'S CHOSEN ONE.

"SURE OF HER SWAY OVER KRISHNA, SHE SAID—

OH KRISHNA I CAN'T WALK ANY MORE. YOU WILL HAVE TO CARRY ME.

YES, DEAR I WILL.

"AND KRISHNA DISAPPEARED. REALISING THAT IT WAS HER VANITY THAT HAD MADE HER LOSE KRISHNA, SHE WAS FILLED WITH REMORSE.

O LORD! WHERE ARE YOU? DON'T LEAVE ME.

" BY THE TIME HER COMPANIONS TOO REACHED THE SPOT, SHE HAD FALLEN IN A SWOON. WHEN REVIVED, SHE SAID—

I INSULTED HIM OUT OF VANITY, SO HE DISAPPEARED.

"THE GOPIKAS WENT FURTHER AND FURTHER IN SEARCH OF KRISHNA.

THE FOREST IS VERY DENSE BEYOND THIS.

YES, IT'S TOO DARK. LET'S GO BACK.

"THEY RETURNED TO THE BANKS OF YAMUNA AND WAITED, SINGING SONGS IN PRAISE OF KRISHNA.

O KRISHNA, HOW WE LONG TO SEE YOU. WE BESEECH YOU TO COME BACK TO US.

"FILLED WITH ANXIETY, MANY OF THEM BURST INTO TEARS. JUST THEN—

"AT THE SIGHT OF THEIR BELOVED KRISHNA, THE GOPIKAS RUSHED TOWARDS HIM.

"LIKE AN ASCETIC WHO HAS ATTAINED SALVATION, SO DID THE GOPIKAS FEEL ENRAPTURED AT THE SIGHT OF KRISHNA.

"SPREADING THEIR VEILS FOR HIM TO SIT, THEY SURROUNDED KRISHNA AND ASKED HIM —

KRISHNA, SOME PEOPLE LOVE ONLY THOSE WHO LOVE THEM. THERE ARE OTHERS WHO LOVE EVEN THOSE WHO DO NOT LOVE THEM. WHILE SOME PEOPLE CANNOT LOVE ANY ONE. WHICH CONDUCT IS CORRECT, ACCORDING TO YOU?

THOSE WHO LOVE, EXPECTING TO BE LOVED IN RETURN, ARE SELFISH. OTHERS WHO LOVE, WITHOUT EXPECTING ANYTHING IN RETURN, ARE SELFLESS AND COMPASSIONATE. THEIR LOVE IS LIKE THAT OF THE PARENTS FOR THE CHILD.

SOME PEOPLE IN THE WORLD SEEM TO BE INCAPABLE OF LOVE. BUT MY DEAR GOPIKAS, I DO NOT BELONG TO ANY OF THESE TYPES.

IF I APPEAR AND DISAPPEAR FROM AMIDST YOU, IT IS ONLY TO TEST YOUR DEVOTION. SEE HOW DEAR I BECAME TO YOU WHEN I WENT AWAY? I AM TOUCHED BY YOUR AFFECTION.

THE GOPIKAS WERE NOW REASSURED, AND STOOD IN A CIRCLE AROUND KRISHNA.

"KRISHNA NOW BEGAN HIS RAS-LILA. MIRACULOUSLY THERE APPEARED ONE KRISHNA BY THE SIDE OF EACH GOPIKA.

THE GOPIKAS, EACH OF THEM, WERE ELATED TO HAVE THEIR BELOVED KRISHNA DANCING NEXT TO THEM.

"THE GENTLE TINKLE OF THEIR BANGLES, THE SOUNDS OF THE TINY BELLS ON THEIR GIRDLES, AND THE ANKLETS ON THEIR LOVELY FEET, FILLED THE AIR AND PROVIDED ACCOMPANIMENT TO THEIR LILTING SONG.

"FASTER AND FASTER THEY DANCED, AS THEIR TRESSES LOOSENED AND THEIR VEILS FLUTTERED IN THE BREEZE.

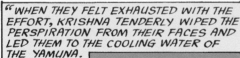

"WHEN THEY FELT EXHAUSTED WITH THE EFFORT, KRISHNA TENDERLY WIPED THE PERSPIRATION FROM THEIR FACES AND LED THEM TO THE COOLING WATER OF THE YAMUNA.

"THE DELIGHTED GOPIKAS SPORTED IN THE RIVER AND MERRILY SPLASHED WATER ON KRISHNA.

"AFTER EMERGING FROM THE RIVER, KRISHNA AND THE GOPIKAS ROAMED ABOUT IN THE GROVE NEARBY. THE SWEET SCENT OF FLOWERS AND THE GENTLE BREEZE REFRESHED THEM.

"RELUCTANT AS THEY WERE TO GO, KRISHNA THEN BADE THE GOPIKAS TO RETURN TO THEIR HOMES.

PAREEKSHIT SAID —

SURELY, LORD KRISHNA WAS BORN TO ELIMINATE SIN FROM EARTH AND ESTABLISH DHARMA. HOW COULD HE THEN BEHAVE THUS WITH THE GOPIKAS?

SHUKADEVA GENTLY EXPLAINED —

WE SHOULD NOT JUDGE THE ACTIONS OF THE LORD BY EARTHLY STANDARDS. HE NEITHER GAINS MERIT BY DOING CERTAIN DEEDS, NOR DOES THE STIGMA OF SIN ATTACH ITSELF TO HIM. HE APPEARS IN HUMAN FORM AND PERFORMS CERTAIN ACTS OR LILAS TO INSPIRE FAITH IN PEOPLE.

THUS ENDS THE THIRD SESSION OF OUR RENDERING OF THE TENTH CHAPTER OF THE BHAGAWAT PURANA.

KRISHNA: VICTORY OVER KAMSA

"PAREEKSHIT WAS ENGROSSED IN LISTENING TO THE NARRATION OF SHUKADEVA.

ON THE AUSPICIOUS DAY OF SHIVARATRI, KRISHNA, NANDA AND OTHER COWHERDS VISITED AMBIKAVANA, A FOREST NEAR BY.

"AFTER A HOLY DIP IN THE RIVER SARASWATI*THEY WORSHIPPED LORD SHIVA.

"ABSTAINING FROM ANY FOOD TO OBSERVE THE SHIVARATRI FAST, THEY WENT TO SLEEP ON THE RIVER BANK. SUDDENLY —

"A HUGE PYTHON POUNCED ON THE SLEEPING NANDA.

HELP, KRISHNA! HELP! HURRY! THE PYTHON IS SWALLOWING ME.

"THE COWHERDS WOKE UP IN ALARM AND FOUND NANDA IN THE COILS OF THE PYTHON.

ATTACK THE PYTHON!

SAVE NANDA!

* A RIVER, WHICH IS SAID TO HAVE JOINED GANGA AND YAMUNA NEAR PRAYAG (ALLAHABAD)

"THEY BEAT THE PYTHON WITH STICKS AND BURNING LOGS, BUT IN VAIN.

"THEN KRISHNA CAME AND GAVE A GENTLE KICK TO THE PYTHON. WITH THE MERE TOUCH OF HIS FOOT, THE PYTHON VANISHED.

"IN ITS PLACE STOOD A YOUTH IN ALL HIS RADIANCE WHO BOWED RESPECTFULLY TO KRISHNA.

WHO ARE YOU? HOW DID A WONDERFUL BEING LIKE YOU ASSUME THE BODY OF A PYTHON?

I AM A VIDYADHARA* NAMED SUDARSHANA. ONE DAY AS I WAS DRIVING IN MY CHARIOT, I SAW SOME RISHIS OF THE ANGIRAS GROUP. PROUD OF MY WEALTH AND GOOD LOOKS, I LAUGHED AT SEEING THEIR UGLY FACES. THEY CURSED ME TO BECOME A PYTHON.

BUT NOW I REALISE HOW FULL OF MERCY THEY WERE. THE MERE TOUCH OF YOUR FOOT HAS RELEASED ME FROM THEIR CURSE. ALLOW ME TO RETURN TO MY WORLD, O LORD.

YOU MAY DO SO.

"BOWING TO KRISHNA, THE YOUTH DISAPPEARED. THE COWHERDS WERE OVERJOYED TO SEE YET ANOTHER MIRACULOUS FEAT PERFORMED BY KRISHNA. THEY RETURNED HOME, LOUDLY SINGING HIS PRAISES.

"ONE DAY KRISHNA AND BALARAMA WERE ROAMING IN THE FOREST ACCOMPANIED BY GOPAS AND GOPIKAS. IT WAS A MOONLIT NIGHT AND THE AIR WAS FILLED WITH THE SCENT OF BLOSSOMS. THE GOPIKAS BURST INTO SONG.

"SO MELODIOUS WAS THEIR MUSIC THAT KRISHNA AND BALARAMA TOO BEGAN TO SING, FILLING THE HEARTS OF THE GOPIKAS WITH JOY. JUST THEN, SHANKHACHOODA, A DEVOTEE OF KUBERA, THE LORD OF WEALTH, APPEARED.

"BEFORE ANYONE KNEW WHAT WAS HAPPENING, SHANKHACHOODA RAN OFF WITH THE GOPIKAS WHO CRIED ALOUD FOR HELP.

OH RAMA!

OH KRISHNA!

"KRISHNA AND BALARAMA LOOKED AROUND FOR A WEAPON.

HERE, KRISHNA. TAKE THIS SALA TREE TO ATTACK HIM.

FEAR NOT, DEAR GOPIKAS. WE ARE COMING TO HELP YOU.

"THE TWO BROTHERS APPROACHING WITH HUGE TREES IN THEIR HANDS LOOKED FEARSOME TO SHANKHACHOODA. ONE LOOK AT THEM AND HE RAN FOR HIS LIFE RELEASING THE GOPIKAS.

BALARAMA, STAY HERE AND PROTECT THE GOPIKAS. I WILL FOLLOW HIM.

"SHANKHACHOODA RAN AS FAST AS HE COULD THROUGH THE FOREST, BUT KRISHNA PURSUED HIM.

I MUST GET HOLD OF HIM AND TAKE HIS CREST JEWEL.

"THEN, WITH A SINGLE STROKE OF HIS HAND, KRISHNA KNOCKED SHANKHACHOODA'S HEAD OFF.

"KRISHNA TOOK THE SHINING GEM THAT WAS ON SHANKHACHOODA'S HEAD AND PRESENTED IT TO BALARAMA.

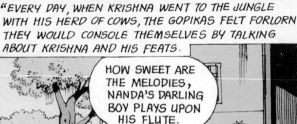

"EVERY DAY, WHEN KRISHNA WENT TO THE JUNGLE WITH HIS HERD OF COWS, THE GOPIKAS FELT FORLORN THEY WOULD CONSOLE THEMSELVES BY TALKING ABOUT KRISHNA AND HIS FEATS.

HOW SWEET ARE THE MELODIES, NANDA'S DARLING BOY PLAYS UPON HIS FLUTE.

EVEN THE DEER AND THE COWS ARE SO CHARMED BY ITS MELODY THAT THEY REMAIN ROOTED TO THE GROUND PRICKING UP THEIR EARS, THEY STAND STILL LIKE A PAINTING ON A WALL.

WITH THE PEACOCK FEATHER TUCKED INTO HIS CURLY LOCKS, BEDECKED WITH FRESH TWIGS, KRISHNA LOOKS LIKE SOME GREAT WRESTLER, AS HE CALLS EACH OF HIS COWS BY THEIR NAMES.

THE VERY WATERS OF THE RIVER SEEM TO RISE AS IF THEY WANT TO GATHER THE DUST FROM HIS FEET.

"ONE DAY, WHEN KRISHNA WAS RETURNING FROM THE FOREST AS USUAL, A HUGE BULL CONFRONTED HIM.

"IT WAS THE DEMON ARISHTASURA IN THE FORM OF A BULL. AS HE STAMPED THE GROUND WITH HIS ENORMOUS HOOVES THE VERY EARTH TREMBLED.

GRRR

"KRISHNA SAW THE FENCES WHICH HAD BEEN DEMOLISHED, AND THE CROPS WHICH HAD BEEN TRODDEN UNDERFOOT BY THE BULL.

HE HAS CAUSED HAVOC EVERYWHERE. SAVE US.

GRRR!

THAT ROAR STRIKES TERROR IN OUR HEARTS!

KRISHNA! KRISHNA! PROTECT US!

"KRISHNA COMFORTED THEM.

BE CALM. THERE IS NOTHING TO FEAR.

O FOOLISH ONE! LEAVE THESE COWS AND COWHERDS ALONE. I AM HERE TO CRUSH THE PRIDE OF WICKED CREATURES LIKE YOU.

"HAVING CHALLENGED THE DEMON, KRISHNA STOOD BY CALMLY, WITH HIS ARM AROUND A FRIEND. THE ENRAGED CREATURE LEAPT TOWARDS KRISHNA.

"HIS HOOVES DIGGING THE GROUND BENEATH, AND HIS RAISED TAIL SCATTERING THE CLOUDS ABOVE, HE RUSHED MENACINGLY AT KRISHNA, LIKE A THUNDERBOLT HURLED BY INDRA.

"KRISHNA CAUGHT HOLD OF HIS HORNS, AND LIKE AN ELEPHANT FIGHTING ITS RIVAL, DROVE THE ASURA BACK FORCEFULLY.

"KRISHNA NOW STEPPED ON THE BODY OF THE DEMON AND TWISTED IT AROUND AS IF HE WERE WRINGING A WET CLOTH.

"WITH A DEFT MOVEMENT, KRISHNA PULLED OUT ITS SHARP HORNS.

"KRISHNA ATTACKED THE DEMON WITH THE HORNS AND KILLED HIM.

"THE COWHERDS GATHERED AROUND KRISHNA AND SANG HIS PRAISES.

"MEANWHILE, NARADA VISITED KAMSA.

KRISHNA, WHO LIVES IN VRAJA, IS THE SON OF DEVAKI WHILE BALARAMA IS ROHINI'S SON. IT WAS TO PROTECT THEM FROM YOU THAT VASUDEVA PLACED THE TWO BOYS IN THE CARE OF HIS FRIEND NANDA. ALL THE ASURAS SENT BY YOU TO KILL THEM HAVE BEEN KILLED THEMSELVES.

"ON HEARING THIS, KAMSA TREMBLED WITH RAGE AND PICKED UP HIS SWORD.

I WILL KILL THAT VASUDEVA.

"NARADA DISSUADED HIM FROM KILLING VASUDEVA. BUT —

THROW VASUDEVA AND DEVAKI IN JAIL AGAIN, BOUND IN FETTERS AND CHAINS.

"AFTER NARADA WENT AWAY, KAMSA CALLED FOR KESHI, AN ASURA.

GO TO VRAJA AND KILL KRISHNA AND BALARAMA.

AS YOU WISH, O KING.

"THEN HE SUMMONED THE HEFTY MUSHTIKA, CHANURA, AND OTHER WRESTLERS, AS WELL AS HIS MINISTERS AND THE KEEPER OF ELEPHANTS.

LISTEN CAREFULLY, O BRAVE CHANURA AND MUSHTIKA IN VRAJA THERE LIVE THE TWO SONS OF VASUDEVA, KRISHNA AND BALARAMA I AM TOLD THEY ARE ORDAINED TO KILL ME.

WHEN THEY ARE BROUGHT HERE, YOU MUST KILL THEM UNDER THE PRETEXT OF WRESTLING WITH THEM.

"HE THEN ADDRESSED THE KEEPER OF ELEPHANTS.

O MAHOUT! LET YOUR ELEPHANT KUVALAYAPEEDA STAND AT THE GATE. AS SOON AS MY ENEMIES COME, THE ELEPHANT CAN KILL THEM.

"THEN HE TURNED TO HIS MINISTERS.

LET PREPARATIONS BE STARTED FOR THE CELE-BRATION OF THE BOW SACRIFICE ON THE EVE OF THE FULL MOON DAY. LET SACRIFICES BE MADE TO LORD SHIVA TO ENSURE OUR SUCCESS.

"THEN KAMSA SENT FOR AKRURA THE YADAVA, A KINSMAN OF KRISHNA.

ONLY YOU AMONG THE YADAVAS HAVE MY WELFARE AT HEART. IT IS TO YOU I TURN FOR HELP JUST AS INDRA TURNS TO VISHNU.

GO TO VRAJA WHERE THE TWO SONS OF VASUDEVA LIVE. TAKE THIS CHARIOT AND FETCH THEM HERE. RIGHT AWAY.

ONCE THEY ARE HERE, I WILL HAVE THEM KILLED BY THE ELEPHANT KUVALAYAPEEDA. IF THEY ESCAPE, MY STRONG WRESTLERS WILL SLAY THEM. THEREAFTER I WILL KILL VASUDEVA AND THE OTHER VRISHNIS, MY OLD FATHER, AND ALL MY ENEMIES.

THEN MY DEAR AKRURA, WITH THE HELP OF FRIENDS LIKE JARASANDHA, MY FATHER-IN-LAW, AND THE ASURAS, I WILL CONQUER THE EARTH. HURRY UP AND FETCH KRISHNA AND BALARAMA. BUT TELL THEM THEY ARE INVITED HERE TO CELEBRATE THE BOW SACRIFICE AND TO SEE THE SIGHTS OF THE CITY OF MATHURA.

INDEED YOU ACT THUS TO AVERT YOUR DEATH. A MAN MUST BE PREPARED FOR BOTH FAILURE AND SUCCESS. I WILL DO AS YOU SAY.

"MEANWHILE, THE DEMON NAMED KESHI ASSUMED THE FORM OF A MIGHTY HORSE AND GALLOPED INTO VRINDAVANA. PAWING THE GROUND IN FURY, HE NEIGHED SO LOUDLY THAT THE PEOPLE TREMBLED IN FEAR.

"HIS HUGE FORM RESEMBLED A MASS OF CLOUD AND HIS MOUTH WAS LIKE THE HOLLOW OF A TREE. THE VERY EARTH QUAKED UNDER HIS FEET. KRISHNA BRAVELY CONFRONTED HIM.

GRRR!

"KESHI RUSHED AT KRISHNA WITH HIS ENORMOUS MOUTH WIDE OPEN AS IF HE WOULD DEVOUR THE ENTIRE SKY. SO FAST WAS HE THAT IT APPEARED IMPOSSIBLE TO CATCH HIM, LET ALONE BRING HIM UNDER CONTROL. HE TRIED TO KICK KRISHNA.

"KRISHNA DEFTLY ELUDED THE BLOW.

"THEN HE CAUGHT HOLD OF THE DEMON BY HIS LEGS, AND THREW HIM SCORNFULLY AT A DISTANCE, LIKE AN EAGLE TOSSING A SERPENT.

"AFTER A WHILE, KESHI PULLED HIMSELF UP AND TRIED TO ATTACK AGAIN. KRISHNA GAZED AT HIM CALMLY WITH A SMILE.

"EFFORTLESSLY HE THRUST HIS LEFT ARM INTO THE OPEN MOUTH OF THE DEMON. HIS DELICATE HAND NOW RESEMBLED A HEATED IRON ROD.

"AT THE TOUCH OF KRISHNA'S HAND KESHI'S TEETH BEGAN TO FALL. THEN KRISHNA'S ARM BEGAN TO SWELL INSIDE THE MOUTH OF THE DEMON. LARGER AND LARGER IT GREW, TILL IT CHOKED THE DEMON'S THROAT.

"KESHI FELL TO THE GROUND THROWING UP HIS LEGS DESPERATELY IN THE AIR. HE COLLAPSED AND HIS SWOLLEN FORM BURST LIKE A RIPE CUCUMBER.

"A FEW DAYS AFTER KILLING KESHI, KRISHNA WAS PLAYING WITH HIS FRIENDS ON A HILLTOP.

LET'S PLAY HIDE AND SEEK. YOU FIVE WILL BE THE THIEVES, SEVEN OF US WILL BE THE GUARDS WHILE THESE LITTLE BOYS WILL BE THE SHEEP.

"THEY WERE DEEPLY ENGROSSED IN THE GAME WHEN VYOMASURA, THE DEMON APPEARED THERE. DISGUISED AS A COWHERD, HE JOINED IN THE GAME AS ONE OF THE THIEVES.

"PRETENDING TO PLAY, HE WOULD TAKE AWAY THE LITTLE BOYS WHO HAD BECOME THE SHEEP.

"ONE BY ONE, HE HID THEM IN A CAVE NEAR BY, COVERING THE MOUTH OF THE CAVE WITH A BIG ROCK.

"AS THE GAME PROGRESSED, THE NUMBER OF PLAYERS DWINDLED TILL THERE WERE ONLY FOUR OR FIVE COWHERDS LEFT. KRISHNA HAD OF COURSE REALISED THE TRUTH.

I WILL CATCH HIM THIS TIME. HIS LITTLE GAME IS OVER NOW.

"AS SOON AS VYOMASURA TRIED TO TAKE AWAY ANOTHER 'SHEEP', KRISHNA POUNCED ON HIM, LIKE A LION ATTACKING A WOLF.

"THE DEMON ASSUMED HIS TRUE FEARSOME FORM.

"BUT MUCH AS HE STRUGGLED, VYOMASURA COULD NOT FREE HIMSELF.

"KRISHNA CAUGHT HIM ROUGHLY AND PINNED HIM DOWN TO THE GROUND.

"HAVING KILLED THE DEMON, KRISHNA WENT FORTH TO THE CAVE WHERE HIS COMPANIONS HAD BEEN HIDDEN BREAKING THE ROCK AT THE ENTRANCE, KRISHNA FREED ALL THE BOYS TRAPPED INSIDE.

"MEANWHILE, AKRURA TOO HAD STARTED FOR VRAJA.

OH, HOW I LONG TO HAVE A GLIMPSE OF LORD KRISHNA KAMSA HAS DONE ME A FAVOUR BY SENDING ME ON THIS MISSION.

"WHEN AT SUNSET HE REACHED HIS DESTINATION, HE SAW KRISHNA AND BALARAMA INSIDE A COW-SHED AKRURA JUMPED DOWN FROM THE CHARIOT AND PROSTRATED HIMSELF AT THEIR FEET.

"THE TWO BROTHERS AFFECTIONATELY LED AKRURA TO THE HOUSE THEREAFTER, HE WAS SERVED A SUMPTUOUS MEAL AND HONOURED AS A WELCOME GUEST NANDA SAID TO AKRURA—

HOW DO YOU SPEND YOUR DAYS IN THE CRUEL RULE OF KAMSA? HIS SUBJECTS ARE LIKE THE SHEEP REARED BY A BUTCHER SO WE WILL NOT DARE ASK WHETHER YOU ARE HAPPY.

"KRISHNA TOO ENQUIRED —

YES, DO TELL US DEAR UNCLE, HOW EVERYONE IS AT MATHURA WE ARE HAPPY INDEED TO SEE YOU HERE DO TELL US THE PURPOSE OF YOUR VISIT.

"AKRURA RELATED THE EVENTS AT MATHURA.

SO WHEN NARADA TOLD KAMSA ABOUT THE TRUTH OF YOUR BIRTH, HE SENT ME HERE TO FETCH YOU ON THE PRETEXT OF INVITING YOU TO A WRESTLING MATCH.

"WHEN THEY HEARD OF KAMSA'S PLAN, KRISHNA AND BALARAMA BURST OUT LAUGHING.

DID YOU HEAR FATHER, WHAT OUR UNCLE KAMSA HAS IN MIND

YES, I DID LET US PREPARE TO LEAVE FOR MATHURA I WILL TELL OUR PEOPLE TO GATHER THE GIFTS FOR KAMSA.

"EARLY NEXT MORNING, AKRURA ASCENDED ONTO HIS CHARIOT TO RETURN TO MATHURA. FOLLOWING HIM WERE CARTS LADEN WITH POTS OF MILK, CURD AND BUTTER, TO BE PRESENTED TO KAMSA. THE COWHERDS SEEMED HAPPY AT THE IDEA OF VISITING MATHURA.

"TO THE GOPIKAS, LOOKING SADLY AT HIM, KRISHNA SAID AFFECTIONATELY WITH A CHARMING SMILE —

I WILL BE BACK SOON.

"HOPING THAT KRISHNA MIGHT CHANGE HIS MIND AND COME BACK, THE GOPIKAS WAITED AWHILE. THEN WITH HEAVY HEARTS, THEY RETURNED TO THEIR HOMES.

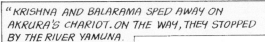

"KRISHNA AND BALARAMA SPED AWAY ON AKRURA'S CHARIOT. ON THE WAY, THEY STOPPED BY THE RIVER YAMUNA.

"AFTER THE TWO BROTHERS HAD REFRESHED THEMSELVES, AKRURA SAID —

I WILL GO AND HAVE A BATH WHILE YOU REST HERE.

"AS HE CEREMONIOUSLY BATHED IN THE WATERS OF THE YAMUNA —

WHY, THERE I CAN SEE KRISHNA AND BALA-RAMA SITTING INSIDE THE WATER. HOW CAN THAT BE! I AM SURE THEY ARE IN THE CHARIOT.

"AKRURA PEEPED OUT OF THE WATER —

YES, THERE THEY ARE, SITTING COMFORTABLY IN THE CHARIOT. DID I IMAGINE THAT THEY WERE INSIDE THE WATER?

"ONCE AGAIN HE DIVED INTO THE WATER. NOW HE BEHELD A SPLENDID SIGHT.

OH! THERE IS THE LORD SHESHA* HIMSELF. NESTLING IN HIS COILS IS KRISHNA, WEARING HIS YELLOW GARMENT DECORATED WITH JEWELS.

"AKRURA WAS OVERWHELMED AT THE SIGHT, AND RESPECTFULLY BOWED BEFORE THEM.

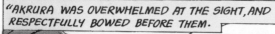

LORD, DIFFERENT PEOPLE WORSHIP YOU IN DIFFERENT WAYS. BUT JUST AS ALL RIVERS FINALLY REACH THE OCEAN, SO ALSO ALL THE DIFFERENT FORMS OF WORSHIP ARE DIRECTED TO YOU.

"JUST AS AN ACTOR HIDES BEHIND A CURTAIN AFTER A PERFORMANCE, LORD KRISHNA WITH-DREW THE VISION INSIDE THE WATER. AKRURA CAME OUT OF THE WATER IN A DAZE—

HAVE YOU SEEN SOMETHING EXTRAORDINARY, UNCLE? WHY ARE YOU LOOKING SO WONDER-STRUCK?

O LORD, ALL THE WONDERFUL THINGS OF THE EARTH, SKY OR OCEAN ARE PRESENT IN YOU. WHAT ELSE IS LEFT FOR ME TO SEE AFTER I HAVE BEHELD YOU.

"WITH THESE WORDS AKRURA DROVE THE CHARIOT AHEAD. BY EVENING THEY REACHED MATHURA. NANDA AND HIS COMPANIONS, WHO HAD GONE AHEAD, MET THEM AT THE CITY GATES. KRISHNA SAID TO AKRURA—

DEAR UNCLE, GO TO YOUR HOUSE. WE WILL GET DOWN HERE TO SEE THE SIGHTS OF THE CITY.

* THE SERPENT ON WHICH VISHNU RESTS

NO, I DO NOT WANT TO GO HOME WITHOUT YOU TWO. PLEASE COME WITH ME AND BLESS OUR HOME WITH YOUR PRESENCE.

INDEED I WILL COME WITH DAU* TO YOUR HOUSE. BUT ONLY AFTER SLAYING KAMSA, THE OPPRESSOR OF THE YADAVAS.

"AKRURA THEN WENT TO KAMSA —

O KING! I HAVE CARRIED OUT YOUR ORDERS. BALARAMA AND KRISHNA HAVE BEEN BROUGHT TO MATHURA.

"MEANWHILE, ACCOMPANIED BY BALARAMA AND OTHER COWHERDS, KRISHNA WENT AROUND THE CITY OF MATHURA.

SEE HOW HIGH THE CRYSTAL GATEWAYS ARE.

EVEN THE HOUSES HAVE BIG GATES EMBOSSED WITH GOLD.

THE BUILDINGS ARE DECORATED WITH CRYSTAL, SAPPHIRES, CORALS, PEARLS AND EMERALDS.

"WHILE THE COWHERDS OF VRAJA WERE ADMIRING THE SIGHTS OF THE CITY OF MATHURA, THEY IN TURN WERE BEING ADMIRED BY THE WOMEN OF MATHURA.

HOW LUCKY ARE THE GOPIKAS OF VRAJA TO BE ABLE TO BEHOLD THESE DELIGHTFUL FACES EVERYDAY.

"AS KRISHNA STRODE ON GRACEFULLY ALONG THE PATH, THEY SHOWERED HIM WITH FLOWERS. SOME OF THEM STOPPED KRISHNA AND BALARAMA TO OFFER WORSHIP.

* THE ADDRESS USED BY KRISHNA FOR BALARAMA

"JUST THEN, KRISHNA SAW A WASHERMAN PASS BY.

WAIT! YOU WILL PROSPER BY GIVING US SUITABLE CLOTHES.

"BUT THE WASHERMAN, A SERVANT OF KAMSA, SAID ANGRILY —

YOU ILL-MANNERED FOOLS! RUN AWAY YOU WHO LIVE IN FORESTS AND MOUNTAINS, HOW CAN YOU THINK OF DRESSING IN SUCH FINE CLOTHES? IF THE KING'S OFFICERS SEE ARROGANT PEOPLE LIKE YOU, THEY WILL TAKE YOU PRISONER AND KILL YOU.

"WHEN THE WASHERMAN SPOKE SO RUDELY, KRISHNA SLAPPED HIM ON HIS FACE.

THE WASHERMAN'S ASSISTANTS FLED IN FRIGHT WHEN THEIR MASTER FELL DOWN.

"KRISHNA PICKED UP THE BUNDLES, THROWN BY THE WASHERMEN AND DISTRIBUTED THE CLOTHES AMONG THE COWHERDS.

HERE, BALARAMA, TAKE THESE.

"WHEN THEY WENT A LITTLE AHEAD, THEY CAME UPON A TAILOR. HE FITTED THE COLOURFUL GARMENTS ON KRISHNA AND THE OTHER COWHERDS, IN A MOST BECOMING FASHION.

"THE DARK KRISHNA AND THE FAIR BALARAMA LOOKED LIKE A PAIR OF ELEPHANTS, ONE BLACK AND THE OTHER WHITE, DECORATED FOR A FESTIVAL. KRISHNA WAS VERY PLEASED WITH THE TAILOR AND BLESSED HIM.

MAY YOU HAVE HEALTH, WEALTH AND PROSPERITY.

"THEREAFTER, KRISHNA AND BALARAMA WENT TO THE HOUSE OF SUDAMA, THE FLOWERMAN, WHO WELCOMED THE TWO BROTHERS AND WORSHIPPED THEM WITH GARLANDS OF FLOWERS, SANDAL-PASTE AND BETEL LEAVES.

O LORD, I AM BLESSED BY THIS VISIT OF YOURS.

"SUDAMA THEN PRESENTED KRISHNA AND BALARAMA WITH GARLANDS OF THE FINEST AND MOST FRAGRANT FLOWERS.

THEREUPON, O PAREEKSHIT, KRISHNA BESTOWED ON SUDAMA SEVERAL BOONS, INCLUDING EVER-GROWING PROSPERITY, LONG LIFE AND FAME.

"AS KRISHNA AND HIS FRIENDS WERE SAUNTERING ALONG ON THE MAIN ROAD OF MATHURA, THEY SAW A BEAUTIFUL WOMAN WITH A HUMPED BACK.

O BEAUTIFUL ONE, WHO ARE YOU? FOR WHOM ARE YOU CARRYING THIS SANDAL-PASTE?

"THE HUNCHBACK WAS COMPLETELY CAPTIVATED BY KRISHNA'S LOOKS, HIS GENTLE SMILE, AND FRIENDLINESS.

MY NAME IS TRIVAKRA, O HANDSOME ONE! I AM A FAVOURITE SERVANT OF KAMSA. I MAKE SPECIAL SANDAL-PASTE AND OINTMENTS FOR HIM.

BUT NONE IS MORE WORTHY OF BEING ANOINTED BY THESE OINTMENTS THAN THE TWO OF YOU. ACCEPT THIS.

"WITH THE YELLOW PASTE CONTRASTING WITH KRISHNA'S DARK COMPLEXION, AND THE RED COLOURED PASTE ON BALARAMA'S FAIR BODY, THEY LOOKED VERY ATTRACTIVE.

I MUST HELP HER BY MAKING HER BODY STRAIGHT.

"KRISHNA PLACED HIS TWO FEET ON THE TOES OF THE HUNCHBACK. HE RAISED HIS HANDS AND WITH HIS FINGERS, HE PUSHED UP HER CHIN WITH A SLIGHT JERK.

"AT THE TOUCH OF HIS HAND, TRIVAKRA LOST HER HUMP, AND STOOD BEFORE HIM, HER BODY ERECT AND WELL PROPOR-TIONED.

"HOLDING A CORNER OF KRISHNA'S GARMENT, SHE SAID —

YOU BOTH MUST COME TO MY HOUSE. I CANNOT GO AWAY LEAVING YOU HERE.

I WILL COME, BUT ONLY AFTER MY TASK IS OVER.

"THUS WITH SWEET WORDS, KRISHNA TOOK LEAVE OF HER.

"AT LAST THEY REACHED THE SITE OF THE SACRIFICE. ON ENTERING, THEY SAW A LARGE AND MIGHTY BOW. RESPLENDENT LIKE A RAINBOW, IT WAS STUDDED WITH EXPENSIVE JEWELS. SEVERAL GUARDS WERE STANDING AROUND, PROTECTING IT. IGNORING THEIR PROTESTS, KRISHNA REACHED FOR THE MIGHTY BOW."

"WITH HIS LEFT HAND HE DEFTLY LIFTED THE BOW, STRUNG IT, AND IN A MATTER OF MINUTES, SPLIT THE BOW INTO TWO."

"BY NOW, THE GUARDS WERE ALERTED, AND SURROUNDED KRISHNA."

CATCH HIM!

DON'T LET HIM GO!

"KRISHNA AND BALARAMA PICKED UP THE PIECES OF THE BOW AND BEGAN TO USE THEM AS WEAPONS."

"AFTER VANQUISHING THE GUARDS WITH THEIR MAKESHIFT WEAPONS, KRISHNA AND BALARAMA STEPPED OUT OF THE HALL AND ROAMED ABOUT."

LOOK AT THESE TWO BRAVE MEN.

SURELY THEY ARE OF DIVINE ORIGIN.

"AT SUNSET, THEY RETURNED TO THEIR CAMP, WHERE THEIR CARTS HAD BEEN KEPT AFTER WASHING UP AND EATING A MEAL OF DELICACIES MADE OF MILK, THEY SLEPT PEACEFULLY.

"MEANWHILE, WHEN KAMSA HEARD THAT KRISHNA AND BALARAMA HAD NOT ONLY BROKEN THE BOW, BUT ALSO KILLED HIS GUARDS WITH EASE, HE WAS WORRIED HE SPENT A SLEEPLESS NIGHT AMIDST SEVERAL ILL OMENS WHEN HE LOOKED IN THE MIRROR—

WHY, I CAN'T SEE MY HEAD IN THE REFLECTION.

"WHEN AT LAST HE DRIFTED INTO A FITFUL SLEEP, HE HAD TERRIBLE NIGHTMARES, AND GOT UP WITH A FRIGHT.

"RECOVERING A LITTLE AT DAWN, KAMSA INAUGURATED THE FESTIVAL OF WRESTLING MATCHES THE PLACE WAS WELL DECORATED WITH GARLANDS, BANNERS AND BUNTING. MELODIOUS MUSIC WAS BEING PLAYED IN THE BACKGROUND.

"BENCHES WERE PROVIDED FOR ALL CITIZENS ON THE HIGHEST POINT WAS PLACED THE ROYAL THRONE FOR KAMSA, WHO WAS STILL IN A DISTURBED STATE.

"THEN CHAMPIONS LIKE CHANURA AND MUSHTIKA, ARRIVED IN THE ARENA ONE BY ONE.

"WHEN KRISHNA ARRIVED AT THE SITE, HE SAW THE ELEPHANT KUVALAYAPEEDA BLOCKING THE ENTRANCE. IN A LOUD VOICE HE CALLED OUT —

O MAHOUT! ALLOW US TO PASS!

"WHEN THERE WAS NO RESPONSE, HE RAISED HIS VOICE IN ANGER.

CAN'T YOU HEAR? MAKE WAY OR I WILL SEND YOU AND YOUR ELEPHANT TO YOUR DEATH.

"THE MAHOUT PROVOKED THE ELEPHANT TO ATTACK KRISHNA THE ENRAGED ELEPHANT WRAPPED HIS TRUNK AROUND KRISHNA.

"BUT HE NIMBLY WRIGGLED OUT OF THE ELEPHANT'S HOLD, AND HID BETWEEN ITS LEGS AFTER GIVING IT A GOOD BLOW.

"THE ELEPHANT WAS FURIOUS AT LOSING SIGHT OF HIS VICTIM, AND BEGAN TO FERRET HIM OUT WITH HIS TRUNK BUT KRISHNA AND BALARAMA TOOK HOLD OF HIS TAIL AND DRAGGED HIM BACK FOR QUITE A DISTANCE.

"FOR LONG, KRISHNA TEASED AND TAUNTED THE ELEPHANT THEN WITH ONE HAND HE PULLED AT THE TRUNK AND FLOORED HIM.

"KRISHNA THEN PULLED OUT THE TUSKS, AND WITH THEM, HE FINISHED OFF BOTH, THE ELEPHANT AND ITS KEEPER.

"HOLDING THE TUSKS ON HIS SHOULDER, KRISHNA ENTERED THE ARENA. PEOPLE OF MATHURA BEGAN TO WHISPER AMONG THEMSELVES.

HE IS THE ONE WHO KILLED POOTANA.

ALSO TRINAVARTA, KESHI AND DHENUKA.

HE IS THE ONE WHO CONQUERED KALIYA.

"ADDRESSING KRISHNA AND BALARAMA, CHANURA, THE ACE WRESTLER, SAID —

WELCOME, KRISHNA AND BALARAMA. OUR KING HAS INVITED YOU HERE TO SHOW YOUR SKILL.

YES CHANURA, WE WOULD LOVE TO DO SO. BUT WE ARE MERE CHILDREN. IT WOULD NOT BE PROPER FOR YOU TO COMPETE WITH YOUNGSTERS.

"CHANURA SAID —

HAH! YOU AND BALARAMA ARE NEITHER CHILDREN NOR YOUNGSTERS. WHY, ONLY MOMENTS AGO YOU PLAYFULLY KILLED THE MIGHTY ELEPHANT KUVALAYAPEEDA. COME ON KRISHNA, TRY YOUR MIGHT ON ME, WHILE BALARAMA FIGHTS MUSHTIKA.

"THE CHALLENGE WAS ACCEPTED. THE FIGHT BEGAN IN EARNEST AS THE PAIR OF WRESTLERS TURNED AND TWISTED, ROLLED AND JUMPED, PULLED AND PUSHED AT EACH OTHER.

"THE AUDIENCE, ESPECIALLY THE WOMEN WERE DISTURBED AS THEY SAW WHAT SEEMED AN UNEQUAL COMBAT.

HOW CAN KING KAMSA ALLOW THIS INJUSTICE?

LET US GO AWAY. I CAN'T BEAR TO SEE THIS.

YES. THESE POOR YOUNG BOYS BEING PITTED AGAINST EXPERT WRESTLERS.

"VASUDEVA AND DEVAKI OVERHEARD THIS CONVERSATION AS THEIR PRISON WAS VERY NEAR THE ARENA. THEY WERE FILLED WITH WORRY AND ANXIETY.

WHAT WILL HAPPEN TO OUR DEAR BOYS.

IMAGINE FIGHTING WITH THOSE POWERFUL MEN.

"BY NOW CHANURA WAS BEGINNING TO REGRET HIS CHALLENGE TO KRISHNA. IN FRUSTRATION, HE ATTACKED KRISHNA ON THE CHEST WITH HIS CLENCHED FISTS.

"UNPERTURBED, KRISHNA CAUGHT HOLD OF HIS ARMS AND FLUNG HIM ON THE GROUND AFTER TURNING HIM AROUND SEVERAL TIMES IN THE AIR.

"MEANWHILE BALARAMA HAD MANAGED TO DEFEAT AND KILL NOT ONLY MUSHTIKA, BUT ALSO KOOTA, WHO CAME TO FIGHT HIM. WITH A SWIFT KICK, KRISHNA BEHEADED SHALA, AND TORE THE BODY OF TOSHALA, THE TWO OTHER WRESTLERS WHO CAME FORWARD.

"CHANURA, MUSHTIKA, KOOTA, SHALA AND TOSHALA— THE FIVE STRONG MEN OF KAMSA—ALL LAY DEAD.

"KAMSA COULD NOT BEAR TO SEE THIS, AND ISSUED A SERIES OF ORDERS TO HIS MEN.

DRIVE THESE TWO SONS OF VASUDEVA OUT OF TOWN. CAPTURE NANDA. TAKE AWAY ALL THE BELONGINGS OF THE COWHERDS. KILL VASUDEVA. KILL UGRASENA TOO.

"EVEN AS KAMSA WAS ISSUING THESE ORDERS, KRISHNA LEAPT UP TO HIS HIGH SEAT. KAMSA TRIED TO DEFEND HIMSELF, BRANDISHING HIS SWORD,

"CATCHING KAMSA BY HIS HAIR KRISHNA THREW HIM DOWN.

"KRISHNA THEN JUMPED ON KAMSA, KILLING HIM THAT VERY INSTANT.

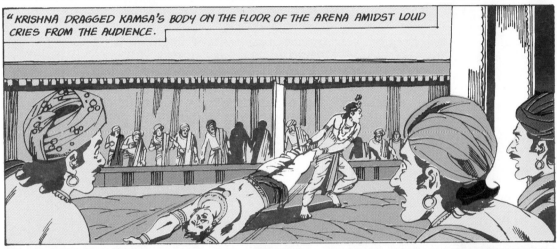

"KRISHNA DRAGGED KAMSA'S BODY ON THE FLOOR OF THE ARENA AMIDST LOUD CRIES FROM THE AUDIENCE.

"KAMSA HAD EIGHT YOUNGER BROTHERS, WHO RUSHED AT KRISHNA AND BALARAMA TO TAKE REVENGE ...

"...BUT BALARAMA KILLED THEM ALL.

THEREAFTER, KRISHNA AND BALARAMA HURRIED TO THE PRISON TO FREE VASUDEVA AND DEVAKI. THOUGH FILLED WITH JOY TO SEE KRISHNA, HIS PARENTS FOUND IT DIFFICULT TO ACCEPT THE LORD AS THEIR OWN SON.

THUS ENDS THE FOURTH SESSION OF OUR RENDERING OF THE TENTH CHAPTER OF THE BHAGAWAT PURANA.

KRISHNA: THE LORD OF DWARAKA

SHUKADEVA CONTINUED HIS NARRATION OF THE EXPLOITS OF YOUNG KRISHNA TO PAREEKSHIT.

AFTER KILLING KAMSA, KRISHNA AND BALARAMA WENT TO MEET VASUDEVA AND DEVAKI AND BOWED RESPECTFULLY BEFORE THEM. THINKING OF THEIR SONS AS THE LORDS OF THE WORLD, VASUDEVA AND DEVAKI FORGOT THAT THEY WERE THEIR SONS.

"KRISHNA DIVINED THE REASON FOR THEIR BEHAVIOUR.

THEY ARE TREATING ME AS GOD, NOT AS THEIR SON.

"KRISHNA USED HIS MAYA* TO MAKE THEM FORGETFUL OF HIS DIVINITY FOR A WHILE.

DEAR FATHER, DEAR MOTHER! WE ARE THE SONS YOU WERE SO ANXIOUS TO MEET. BUT ALAS, WE HAD BEEN SEPARATED FROM YOU IN OUR INFANCY AND BOYHOOD.

WE FEEL WE HAVE LIVED IN VAIN SINCE WE HAVE NOT BEEN ABLE TO SERVE YOU. THAT CRUEL KAMSA TREATED YOU VERY BADLY, YET WE COULD DO NOTHING TO HELP YOU.

"OVERWHELMED BY KRISHNA'S WORDS, VASUDEVA CLASPED KRISHNA IN A FOND EMBRACE.

* ILLUSORY POWER

"AFTER COMFORTING HIS PARENTS, KRISHNA WENT TO HIS GRANDFATHER UGRASENA WHO HAD BEEN KEPT IN PRISON BY KAMSA.

YOU ARE NOW THE KING OF THE YADAVAS. TREAT ME AS ONE OF YOUR SUBJECTS.

"KAMSA'S CRUEL REIGN HAD MADE MANY OF HIS SUBJECTS FLEE TO THE NEIGHBOURING KINGDOMS. KRISHNA WELCOMED THEM BACK AND SETTLED THEM IN THEIR OWN HOMES.

NOT ONLY ARE WE BACK HOME BUT WE HAVE BEEN GIVEN ENOUGH WEALTH TO START LIFE ALL OVER AGAIN.

YES, NOW THAT KAMSA IS KILLED WE CAN LOOK FORWARD TO A SAFE AND JOYFUL LIFE UNDER KRISHNA'S PROTECTION.

"THEN KRISHNA AND BALARAMA WENT TO MEET NANDA.

FATHER, PLEASE PROCEED TO VRINDAVANA. WE WILL COME TO MEET YOU AS SOON AS OUR WORK HERE IS OVER.

"NANDA HUGGED THE BOYS TENDERLY AND MADE PREPARATIONS TO RETURN HOME WITH HIS COWHERDS.

"THEREAFTER AT THE REQUEST OF VASUDEVA, GARGA-CHARYA PERFORMED THE UPANAYANA* CEREMONY OF BALARAMA AND KRISHNA.

✱ THREAD CEREMONY.

NOW I WILL TELL YOU THE GAYATRI MANTRA IN YOUR EAR.

"KRISHNA AND BALARAMA THEN SET OUT FOR THE ASHRAMA OF SAGE SANDIPANI IN AVANTI *

"WITH SAGE SANDIPANI AS THEIR GURU, THE BOYS BEGAN THEIR FORMAL EDUCATION.

"THE GURU TAUGHT THEM THE VEDAS. HE ALSO TAUGHT THEM HOW TO WIELD WEAPONS AND ALL THE SIXTY-FOUR ARTS.

"SO ATTENTIVE WERE THE BOYS, THAT THEY LEARNT EACH SUBJECT THE FIRST TIME IT WAS TAUGHT TO THEM.

"THUS WITHIN SIXTY-FOUR DAYS, THEY MASTERED ALL THE SIXTY-FOUR ARTS AND CRAFTS.

"AT THE END OF THEIR TRAINING, THEY HUMBLY ADDRESSED THEIR GURU.

TRADITION DEMANDS THAT WE OFFER YOU A GURUDAKSHINA*, NOW THAT WE HAVE COMPLETED OUR EDUCATION. PLEASE TELL US WHAT TRIBUTE WOULD YOU LIKE US TO OFFER YOU?

"GURU SANDIPANI WAS AWARE OF THE EXTRAORDINARY POWERS OF HIS PUPILS. AFTER CONSULTING HIS WIFE HE SAID —

RESTORE TO ME MY SON, WHO WAS DROWNED IN PRABHASA.

I WILL.

"THE BOYS CLIMBED ONTO THEIR CHARIOT AND WENT TO PRABHASA.** THEY SAT ON THE SEASHORE FOR A WHILE.

"ASSUMING THE FORM OF A HUMAN, THE OCEAN APPEARED BEFORE KRISHNA. KRISHNA ADDRESSED THE GOD OF THE OCEAN THUS —

O KING OF THE OCEANS, RETURN TO US THE SON OF OUR GURU, WHOM YOU HAD SWEPT AWAY FROM THIS VERY SPOT.

* OFFERING MADE TO THE TEACHER   ** IN GUJARAT

"THE OCEAN REPLIED —

O LORD, IT WAS NOT I WHO TOOK HIM AWAY. THERE IS A MIGHTY ASURA CALLED PANCHAJANA WHO DWELLS IN MY WATERS IN THE GUISE OF A CONCH-SHELL. IT WAS HE WHO TOOK THE BOY AWAY.

"AS SOON AS HE HEARD THIS, KRISHNA DIVED INTO THE SEA.

"AFTER MOMENTS HE CAME UP —

I KILLED THE ASURA BUT I COULD NOT FIND THE BOY. HERE IS THE SHELL IN WHICH THE DEMON LIVED.

"THIS CONCH-SHELL CAME TO BE KNOWN AS PANCHAJANYA.

"KRISHNA AND BALARAMA THEN WENT TO THE ABODE OF YAMA, THE LORD OF DEATH. KRISHNA BLEW ON THE PANCHAJANYA TO ANNOUNCE HIS ARRIVAL.

"ON HEARING THE SOUND OF THE CONCH-SHELL, YAMA CAME TO MEET THEM.

WELCOME TO MY KINGDOM. O KRISHNA AND BALA-RAMA. WHAT CAN I DO FOR YOU?

MY GURU'S SON HAS BEEN BROUGHT HERE. OBEY MY COMMAND AND BRING HIM TO ME.

"SOON —

HERE HE IS.

KRISHNA AND BALARAMA WENT BACK TO SANDIPANI'S ASHRAM WITH THE BOY.

GURUDEVA, WHAT ELSE CAN WE DO FOR YOU?

NO, YOU HAVE DONE ALL YOU CAN. GO NOW TO YOUR OWN HOMES. MAY YOUR KNOWLEDGE REMAIN EVER FRESH.

WITH THE BLESSING OF THEIR GURU, THE TWO BOYS RETURNED TO MATHURA.

WELCOME BACK, O KRISHNA!

WE FEEL AS IF WE HAVE REGAINED OUR LOST WEALTH.

O PAREEKSHIT, UDDHAVA WAS A DEAR FRIEND OF SHRI KRISHNA, AND A RESPECTED MINISTER TOO. ONE DAY KRISHNA BADE HIM TO GO TO VRINDAVANA.

DEAR UDDHAVA, GO TO MY PARENTS NANDA AND YASHODA. TELL THEM I AM WELL.

THE GOPIKAS OF VRINDAVANA ARE VERY MUCH ATTACHED TO ME. THEY MUST BE MISSING ME AND EAGERLY AWAITING MY RETURN. GO AND CONSOLE THEM.

I WILL LEAVE AT ONCE.

"WHEN UDDHAVA REACHED VRINDAVANA IT WAS DUSK, THE TIME FOR THE COWS TO RETURN FROM GRAZING IN THE WOODS. THE DUST RAISED BY THEIR HOOVES ENVELOPED HIS CHARIOT.

"THE SOUND OF THE CALVES LOWING MINGLED WITH THE MELODIOUS MUSIC OF THE FLUTES. LAMPS SHONE IN THE HOMES. THE AIR WAS FILLED WITH INCENSE.

"NANDA WELCOMED UDDHAVA AS IF HE WERE HIS OWN SON.

"AFTER HE HAD BEEN FED A SUMPTUOUS MEAL AND SEATED COMFORTABLY, NANDA ASKED HIM EAGERLY —

DOES KRISHNA REMEMBER US AT ALL? DOES HE MISS HIS PARENTS AND HIS FRIENDS? OH! IF HE WOULD ONLY COME ONCE TO MEET US. WE DO SO LONG TO BEHOLD HIS BEAUTIFUL FACE AND HIS ENDEARING SMILE.

"NANDA'S EYES MOISTENED WITH UNSHED TEARS.

WE MISS HIM SO MUCH. EVERY-THING IN VRINDAVANA REMINDS US OF HIM —THE RIVERS, THE MOUNTAINS, THE COWS, THE COW-HERDS.

"SOON TEARS BEGAN TO TRICKLE DOWN NANDA'S FACE. YASHODA TOO BEGAN TO CRY. UDDHAVA SAID —

INDEED, YOU BOTH ARE THE LUCKIEST OF PEOPLE TO HAVE SUCH LOVE AND DEVOTION TOWARDS KRISHNA. HE WILL SOON BE WITH YOU.

"UDDHAVA AND NANDA SPENT THE WHOLE NIGHT PRAISING KRISHNA AND HIS DEEDS.

"EARLY MORNING THE GOPIKAS AROSE TO DO THEIR CHORES.

"WHEN THE SUN ROSE, THEY NOTICED A GOLDEN CHARIOT ON NANDA'S DOORSTEP.

WHOSE COULD IT BE?

I HOPE IT IS NOT AKRURA WHO TOOK AWAY OUR BELOVED KRISHNA.

"WHILE THEY WERE SPEAKING THUS, THEY SAW UDDHAVA AT A DISTANCE.

LOOK AT THAT STRANGER. HE IS BUILT AND DRESSED LIKE OUR BELOVED KRISHNA.

"THE CURIOUS GOPIKAS SURROUNDED UDDHAVA AND PLIED HIM WITH QUESTIONS.

WHERE HAVE YOU COME FROM?

WHY ARE YOU HERE?

"WHEN THEY LEARNT THAT UDDHAVA WAS AN EMISSARY OF KRISHNA, THEY QUICKLY TOOK HIM ASIDE.

OH! YOU HAVE COME WITH A MESSAGE FROM YOUR LORD. BUT HE MUST HAVE SENT YOU TO COMFORT HIS PARENTS FOR THERE IS NOTHING ELSE HERE WORTHWHILE FOR HIM TO REMEMBER.

ONLY THE PARENTAL BOND ENDURES, ALL OTHER RELATION- SHIPS ARE WEAK AND SHORT LIVED. CITIZENS ABANDON A KING WHO BECOMES WEAK. STUDENTS FORSAKE THEIR TEACHER WHEN THEIR STUDIES ARE OVER. WHY, EVEN BIRDS FLY AWAY FROM THE TREE WHEN ITS FRUITS ARE EXHAUSTED.

"THE GOPIKAS WERE SO THRILLED AT THE ARRIVAL OF KRISHNA'S MESSENGER THAT THEY BABBLED INCOHERENTLY —

TELL US HOW OUR KRISHNA IS? DOES HE EVEN MENTION US? WILL WE EVER HAVE THE GOOD FORTUNE OF SEEING HIM AGAIN?

"UDDHAVA WAS MOVED BY THE DEVOTION OF THE WOMEN.

YOU ARE FORTUNATE TO BE SO CLOSE TO LORD KRISHNA. YOUR DEVOTION CAN SERVE AS AN INSPIRING EXAMPLE FOR LEARNED SAGES. THAT IS WHY, KRISHNA HAS SENT ME HERE WITH A MESSAGE.

"UDDHAVA THEN RELATED THE MESSAGE OF KRISHNA TO THE ANXIOUS WOMEN.

YOU CAN NEVER REALLY BE SEPARATED FROM ME FOR I AM EVERYWHERE. I PERVADE THE ENTIRE UNIVERSE IN DIFFERENT FORMS. I AM THE CREATOR, SUSTAINER AND DESTROYER. I AM THE ETERNAL SOUL.

JUST AS ALL RIVERS, ULTIMATELY REACH THE OCEAN AFTER MEANDERING ON THEIR COURSE, SO ALSO VARIOUS FORMS OF WORSHIP CULMINATE IN THE DESIRE TO ATTAIN ME. SEPARATION FROM ME WILL MAKE YOUR LOVE MORE INTENSE. BUT I CAN NEVER FORSAKE YOU. BE ASSURED.

"FOR MANY MONTHS UDDHAVA STAYED IN VRINDAVANA REGALING THE PEOPLE WITH STORIES OF KRISHNA'S DEEDS.

" WHEN AT LAST UDDHAVA WAS ABOUT TO RETURN TO MATHURA, THE PEOPLE OF VRINDAVANA PRESENTED HIM WITH GIFTS AND BADE HIM A TEARFUL FAREWELL.

DEAR UDDHAVA, OUR ONLY DESIRE IS TO DEDICATE ALL OUR THOUGHTS AND ACTIONS TO LORD KRISHNA.

"UDDHAVA RETURNED TO MATHURA AND TOLD HIM WHAT HE HAD HEARD AND SEEN IN VRINDAVANA.

SO ENGROSSED ARE THE GOPIKAS IN YOU, THAT THEY SEE YOU EVERYWHERE, IN ALL OBJECTS AND BEINGS. PEOPLE IN VRINDAVANA PINE TO HAVE A GLIMPSE OF YOU.

"AFTER THEY HAD DELIVERED THE PRE-SENTS SENT BY NANDA TO VASUDEVA, BALARAMA AND KING UGRASENA, KRISHNA REMEMBERED A PROMISE MADE EARLIER.

I TOLD SAIRANDHRI* THAT I WOULD VISIT HER HOUSE AFTER MY MISSION HERE WAS OVER. COME LET'S GO NOW.

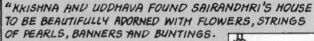

"KRISHNA AND UDDHAVA FOUND SAIRANDHRI'S HOUSE TO BE BEAUTIFULLY ADORNED WITH FLOWERS, STRINGS OF PEARLS, BANNERS AND BUNTINGS.

LORD KRISHNA? AT MY DOOR-STEP.

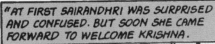

"AT FIRST SAIRANDHRI WAS SURPRISED AND CONFUSED. BUT SOON SHE CAME FORWARD TO WELCOME KRISHNA.

WELCOME, O LORD!

"AFTER A WHILE SHE BEDECKED HERSELF WITH BEAUTIFUL GARMENTS AND ORNAMENTS AND SAT WITH HER GUESTS.

DEAR KRISHNA, STAY HERE WITH ME FOR A FEW DAYS. I CANNOT BEAR TO LET YOU GO NOW.

I MUST LEAVE NOW.

"LATER ONE DAY HE VISITED AKRURA WITH BALARAMA AND UDDHAVA. AKRURA RAN FORWARD TO WELCOME THEM.

WELCOME! I AM FORTUNATE TO HAVE YOU AS MY GUESTS.

YOU TWO HAVE BEEN BORN ON EARTH TO RID IT OF WICKEDNESS.

YOU ARE OUR UNCLE AND WELL-WISHER. INDEED YOU ARE ONE OF OUR CLOSEST FRIENDS. THAT IS WHY I WANT YOU TO GO TO HASTINAPURA AND MEET THE PANDAVAS.

AFTER THE DEATH OF THEIR FATHER PANDU, YUDHISH-THIRA AND HIS BROTHERS HAVE GONE TO HASTINA-PURA TO THEIR UNCLE DHRITA-RASHTRA. HIS SON DURYODHANA IS WICKED.

THEREFORE I AM ANXIOUS ABOUT THE PANDAVAS. I WOULD LIKE TO ENSURE THEIR HAPPINESS.

"AS REQUESTED BY KRISHNA, AKRURA WENT TO HASTINAPURA AND MET DHRITARASHTRA, BHEESHMA VIDURA AND THE PANDAVAS.

"FOR THE NEXT FEW MONTHS, AKRURA STAYED AT HASTINAPURA TO FIND OUT HOW DHRITARASHTRA WAS TREATING THE PANDAVAS.

WHY, DHRITARASHTRA DOES NOT DARE TO DO ANYTHING AGAINST THE WISHES OF HIS WICKED SONS.

THAT VILE SHAKUNI IS ALSO A BAD INFLUENCE ON THE OLD KING.

"AKRURA SPOKE TO HIS COUSIN KUNTI.

YES IT IS TRUE THAT MY SONS ARE TREATED BADLY. DURYODHANA IS JEALOUS OF THEM AND RESENTS THEIR POPULARITY WITH THE PEOPLE.

"VIDURA WHO WAS ALSO PRESENT ADDED —

INDEED IN VALOUR, STRENGTH AND MANNERS, THE PANDAVAS ARE FAR SUPERIOR TO THE KAURAVA BROTHERS.

DURYODHANA AND HIS BROTHERS ARE FOREVER PLOTTING TO HARM THE PANDAVAS. THEY EVEN TRIED TO POISON THEM.

"BEFORE LEAVING, AKRURA ADDRESSED THE COURT AT HASTINAPURA AND CONVEYED THE MESSAGE OF KRISHNA AND BALARAMA.

MAY YOU ENHANCE THE GLORY OF THE KURU CLAN. STRIVE TO KEEP YOUR SUBJECTS HAPPY. TREAT ALL YOUR KITH AND KIN ALIKE. BE IMPARTIAL IN YOUR BEHAVIOUR TOWARDS YOUR SONS AND THE PANDAVAS.

"KING DHRITARASHTRA REPLIED.

O AKRURA, I KNOW YOU MEAN WELL. BUT MY HEART IS ALREADY SO BIASED TOWARDS MY SONS, THAT YOUR GOOD COUNSEL HAS NO EFFECT. I HEAR THAT GOD HIMSELF HAS BEEN INCARNATED IN THE YADAVA DYNASTY FOR RIDDING THE WORLD OF EVIL. LET HIS WILL BE DONE.

"AKRURA RETURNED TO MATHURA AND REPORTED TO KRISHNA.

NOW THAT I HAVE OBSERVED HIS BEHAVIOUR MYSELF, THERE IS NO DOUBT THAT DHRITARASHTRA FAVOURS THE KAURAVAS AND THE PANDAVAS ARE NOT TREATED FAIRLY.

MEANWHILE, KAMSA'S TWO QUEENS ASTI AND PRAPTI, WENT BACK TO THEIR FATHER'S HOUSE AFTER THE DEATH OF THEIR HUSBAND. THEY TOLD THEIR FATHER, JARASANDHA, THE KING OF MAGADHA, HOW KAMSA HAD BEEN KILLED.

"JARASANDHA WAS ENRAGED --

SO, FATHER, AFTER KILLING THE MIGHTY WRESTLERS KRISHNA KILLED OUR DEAR HUSBAND.

I WILL PUNISH HIM.

"JARASANDHA WAS FILLED WITH BITTERNESS AND SORROW.

LET MY ARMY PREPARE FOR WAR. I WILL NOT REST TILL I WIPE OUT THE ENTIRE RACE OF THE YADAVAS FROM THE FACE OF THE EARTH.

"SOON, WITH AN ARMY OF 23 AKSHAUHINIS*, JARASANDHA SURROUNDED THE CITY OF MATHURA, THE CAPITAL OF THE YADAVAS. KRISHNA BEHELD THE AWESOME SIGHT.

WHY, JARASANDHA'S ARMY LOOKS LIKE A VERITABLE OCEAN OF SOLDIERS AROUND OUR CITY.

PERHAPS, IT IS GOOD THAT JARASANDHA HAS COLLECTED THIS LARGE ARMY AND BROUGHT THEM TO MY DOOR. I CAN DESTROY THEM ALL AT ONCE AND LIGHTEN THE BURDEN OF EVIL FROM THE EARTH.

BUT I WILL NOT KILL JARASANDHA YET. LET HIM COLLECT MORE OF HIS MEN TO ATTACK ME. I CAN KILL THEM TOO AND FULFIL THE PURPOSE OF MY INCARNATION.

"WHILE KRISHNA WAS ENGROSSED IN THOUGHT, TWO GLEAMING CHARIOTS DESCENDED FROM THE SKY. THEY WERE DRIVEN BY ABLE CHARIOTEERS AND EQUIPPED WITH WONDERFUL WEAPONS OF ALL DESCRIPTION.

BEHOLD, DEAR BROTHER!

* DIVISION OF THE ARMY CONTAINING.. 21870 ELEPHANTS, 21870 CHARIOTS, 65610 CAVALRY AND 109350 INFANTRY

"THE CELESTIAL AND ETERNAL WEAPONS OF BALARAMA ALSO APPEARED THAT VERY INSTANCE.

NOT ONLY THE CHARIOTS, EVEN YOUR FAVOURITE WEAPONS— THE PLOUGH AND THE PESTLE ARE HERE.

GO FORTH ON THIS CHARIOT AND DESTROY THE ENEMY.

PROTECT OUR PEOPLE FROM THIS CALAMITY. FOR WE ARE HERE ON EARTH TO PROTECT THE GOOD AND DESTROY THE WICKED.

"KRISHNA AND BALARAMA THEN DONNED THEIR ARMOUR AND ASCENDED THE CELESTIAL CHARIOTS.

THERE WAS ONLY A SMALL ARMY WITH THEM. ON THE OUTSKIRTS OF THE CITY, KRISHNA BLEW HIS CONCH-SHELL, THE PANCHAJANYA.

" THE SOUND WAS LOUD ENOUGH TO PUT FEAR IN THE HEARTS OF THE BRAVEST OF WARRIORS IN JARASANDHA'S ARMY.

"JARASANDHA SAID TO KRISHNA —

O KRISHNA, YOU ARE A MERE LAD. I FEEL EMBARRASSED TO FIGHT WITH YOU ALONE.

" THEN JARASANDHA TURNED TO BALARAMA —

BALARAMA, IF YOU BELIEVE THAT DEATH ON THE BATTLE-FIELD WILL ENSURE YOU A PLACE IN HEAVEN, COME FIGHT WITH ME.

" KRISHNA CALMLY RESPONDED —

TRUE WARRIORS DON'T BRAG LIKE YOU, THEY JUST ACT. GO AHEAD! YOUR WORDS DON'T BOTHER ME.

JUST AS CLOUDS COVERING THE SUN OR SMOKE ENVELOP-ING A FIRE CANNOT DO SO FOR LONG, SO ALSO THE ENORMOUS ARMY OF JARASANDHA COULD NOT SURROUND BALARAMA AND KRISHNA FOR LONG.

"THE WOMEN OF MATHURA WERE ANXIOUSLY WATCHING THE SCENE FROM THEIR BALCONIES AND TERRACES.

SEE! JARASANDHA'S SOLDIERS HAVE CROWDED IN FROM ALL SIDES.

WE CANNOT EVEN GET A GLIMPSE OF KRISHNA'S ARMY NOW.

OH! THE CHARIOT OF KRISHNA WITH THE PENNANT OF GARUDA HAS DISAPPEARED.

THE FLAG OF PALM ATOP BALARAMA'S CHARIOT IS NOT SEEN EITHER.

"FEARING THE WORST, THE WOMEN BEGAN TO SOB LOUDLY.

"THE ARROWS OF JARASANDHA'S SOLDIERS WERE FALLING ON KRISHNA'S ARMY LIKE RAIN-DROPS DURING A DOWNPOUR. KRISHNA NOW PICKED UP HIS BOW.

"HE BEGAN SENDING SHOWER AFTER SHOWER OF ARROWS AT JARASANDHA'S ARMY.

"THE SPEED WITH WHICH KRISHNA REMOVED THE ARROWS FROM HIS QUIVER, STRINGED HIS BOW, AND SHOT THE ARROWS, WAS SO RAPID IT LOOKED AS IF A WHEEL WAS BEING TURNED.

"SOON JARASANDHA'S ARMY BEGAN TO SUCCUMB TO THE ONSLAUGHT OF KRISHNA'S ARROWS.

"ELEPHANTS WERE BEHEADED AND HORSES TUMBLED DOWN. CHARIOTS TOO WERE SMASHED BY KRISHNA'S POWERFUL ARROWS.

"MEANWHILE BALARAMA WAS ATTACKING THE ARMY USING HIS AWESOME PESTLE AS A WEAPON.

"THOUGH JARASANDHA'S ARMY WAS HUGE AND WELL-EQUIPPED, KRISHNA AND BALARAMA DESTROYED IT EFFORTLESSLY.

"BEREFT OF EVEN HIS CHARIOT, ALL JARASANDHA HAD LEFT WAS HIS LIFE.

"BALARAMA POUNCED ON HIM AND WAS ABOUT TO KILL HIM BUT KRISHNA INTERVENED.

STOP, BALARAMA! LET HIM GO.

LET HIM GO AND COLLECT ANOTHER ARMY. WE WILL DESTROY THAT TOO.

"JARASANDHA'S MIGHT AS A WARRIOR HAD EARNED HIM THE RESPECT OF MANY A VALOROUS HERO. NOW HE FELT HUMILIATED.

KRISHNA TOOK PITY ON ME AND LET ME GO. WHAT A DIS-HONOUR IT IS FOR ME.

"JARASANDHA SET OUT FOR HIS KINGDOM, ALONG WITH THE REMNANTS OF HIS ARMY.

I MUST DO SEVERE PENANCE TO ATONE FOR THIS EMBARRASSMENT.

"BUT SOME OF THE KINGS WHO HAD FOUGHT ALONG WITH HIM DISSUADED HIM.

THE YADAVAS CANNOT REALLY DEFEAT YOU. IT IS JUST DESTINY THAT YOU HAD TO FEEL HUMILIATED.

IT WAS GOD'S WILL THAT YOU FACE DEFEAT THIS TIME. BUT YOU CAN SURELY WIN THE NEXT TIME. DON'T THINK OF RETIRING TO THE FOREST.

"WHILE MOST OF JARASANDHA'S ARMY HAD BEEN ANNIHILATED, KRISHNA'S ARMY WAS ALMOST UNSCATHED. THEY WERE FETED AND WELCOMED BY THE CITIZENS OF MATHURA.

"THE VICTORIOUS ARMY WAS RECEIVED WITH A SHOWER OF FLOWERS BY THE ADMIRING CITIZENS.

"THEY HAD COLLECTED A HUGE NUMBER OF PRECIOUS STONES, GEMS AND ORNA-MENTS FROM THE VANQUISHED ARMY. THESE WERE PRESENTED TO KING UGRASENA.

"AS KRISHNA HAD PREDICTED, JARASANDHA GATHERED ANOTHER ARMY OF 23 AKSHAUHINIS AND ATTACKED MATHURA AGAIN.

"SEVENTEEN TIMES JARASANDHA ATTACKED MATHURA WITH A HUGE ARMY AND SEVENTEEN TIMES HIS ARMY WAS DESTROYED.

"ON THE EIGHTEENTH OCCASION, JUST BEFORE JARASANDHA REACHED MATHURA, THE ASURA KALAYAVANA, HEARD OF THE MIGHT OF KRISHNA AND BALARAMA.

THEY SAY THE YADAVAS ARE AS MIGHTY AS I AM. LET ME GO AND CONFRONT THEM.

"KALAYAVANA WAS A MIGHTY ASURA WHOM EVEN INTREPID WARRIORS FEARED TO FACE. HE NOW ATTACKED MATHURA WITH A BIG ARMY.

"KRISHNA SAID TO BALARAMA —

OH! NOW WE HAVE TO FACE TWO ENEMIES, JARASANDHA AND KALAYAVANA.

IF BOTH OF US ARE BUSY REPELLING KALAYAVANA'S FORCES AND JARASANDHA ALSO ATTACKS, HE MAY OVERPOWER OUR PEOPLE.

WE MUST HAVE AN INVINCIBLE FORTRESS BUILT WHERE NO ENEMY CAN ENTER. ONLY AFTER PLACING OUR PEOPLE INSIDE SUCH A FORTRESS, WILL WE FIGHT KALAYAVANA.

"AFTER CONSULTING BALARAMA, KRISHNA HAD SUCH A STRONG FORT CITY BUILT IN THE OCEAN. IT WAS A WONDER OF ARCHITECTURE AND CRAFTSMANSHIP WITH WIDE ROADS, LOVELY GARDENS AND HUGE GATEWAYS.

"IN THE MIDST OF THE WELL-PLANNED HOUSES WERE THE GOLDEN PALACES OF KING UGRASENA, VASUDEVA, BALARAMA AND KRISHNA. THE CITY WAS NAMED DWARAKA.

"THE DEVAS SENT MANY GIFTS FOR THIS NEW CITY. INDRA SENT AN ASSEMBLY ROOM CALLED SUDHARMA SABHA. PEOPLE SEATED IN THAT ROOM WERE NOT AFFECTED BY EARTHLY NEEDS LIKE HUNGER AND THIRST.

"VARUNA SENT A NUMBER OF WHITE HORSES, SWIFT AND SURE-FOOTED.

"WITH HIS DIVINE POWER KRISHNA TRANSPORTED HIS KITH AND KIN TO DWARAKA, THE NEWLY CREATED CITY.

"LEAVING THE REST OF HIS SUBJECTS IN MATHURA, IN BALARAMA'S CARE, KRISHNA CAME OUT OF THE MAIN GATE OF MATHURA. HE WAS UNARMED. A GARLAND OF LOTUSES ADORNED HIS NECK.

"KALAYAVANA, WHO WAS STATIONED OUTSIDE THE GATE, BEHELD THE APPROACHING FIGURE.

SURELY THIS MUST BE KRISHNA. HE FITS THE DESCRIPTION NARADA GAVE ME OF KRISHNA.

BUT HE IS APPROACH-ING ME UNARMED. I TOO MUST PUT AWAY MY WEAPONS.

"BUT WHEN KALAYAVANA CAME NEAR, KRISHNA TURNED AWAY AND BEGAN TO RUN.

"KALAYAVANA TOO BEGAN TO FOLLOW HIM AT A RAPID PACE.

"FOR LONG KALAYAVANA CHASED THE FLEEING KRISHNA HOPING TO CATCH HIM.

DON'T RUN AWAY FROM THE BATTLEFIELD! YOU ARE A DESCENDANT OF THE BRAVE YADAVAS.

"BUT KRISHNA PAID NO HEED AND RAN ON TILL THEY CAME UPON A HILLSIDE CAVE.

"EVEN AS KALAYAVANA TRIED TO RESTRAIN HIM WITH SHOUTS KRISHNA ENTERED THE DARK CAVE.

STOP! STOP!

"KALAYAVANA TOO DUCKED INTO THE CAVE.

"IN THE DIM LIGHT KALAYAVANA SAW A SLEEPING FORM.

JUST LOOK AT HIM! HE MADE ME RUN SO FAR AND NOW HE IS LYING DOWN WITHOUT A CARE.

"IN ANGER, KALAYAVANA GAVE A SWIFT KICK.

"THE SLEEPING MAN SLOWLY WOKE UP. WHEN HE OPENED HIS EYES FULLY, HE SAW KALAYAVANA BEFORE HIM.

"AS SOON AS HIS GAZE FELL ON KALAYAVANA, THE MIGHTY ASURA CAUGHT FIRE...

...AND WAS REDUCED TO A HEAP OF ASHES.

INTRIGUED BY THE NARRATION, PAREEKSHIT INTERRUPTED SHUKADEVA —

WHO WAS THAT MAN? HOW DID HE GET SUCH POWER? WHY WAS HE SLEEPING IN THE CAVE?

SHUKADEVA EXPLAINED —

HE WAS KING MUCHUKUNDA, OF THE IKSHVAKU DYNASTY. HE ONCE PROTECTED THE DEVAS FROM THE ATTACK OF THE ASURAS. PLEASED WITH HIS SERVICE, THE DEVAS GRANTED HIM A BOON.

THIS LONG BATTLE WITH THE ASURAS HAS MADE ME WEARY. I JUST WANT TO SLEEP.

"THE DEVAS GRANTED HIS SIMPLE WISH BUT ADDED —

IF ANY FOOL DISTURBS YOUR SLEEP, HE WILL BE REDUCED TO ASHES THE INSTANT YOU LOOK AT HIM.

"KALAYAVANA WAS DESTROYED. KRISHNA SUDDENLY APPEARED BEFORE KING MUCHUKUNDA. HE WAS TAKEN ABACK AT THE SUDDEN APPEARANCE OF KRISHNA'S RESPLENDENT FORM.

WHO ARE YOU? WHY ARE YOU ROAMING IN THIS JUNGLE?

ARE YOU AGNI, THE LORD OF FIRE? OR SOME OTHER GOD?

INDEED YOU MUST BE NARAYANA, SINCE YOUR RADIANCE IS LIGHTING UP THIS DARK CAVE.

"KRISHNA REPLIED WITH A SMILE.

I HAVE COUNTLESS NAMES. IT MAY BE POSSIBLE TO COUNT THE PARTICLES OF DUST ON EARTH. BUT MY NAMES AND FORMS CANNOT BE ENUMERATED.

NOW I HAVE APPEARED ON EARTH IN VASUDEVA'S HOUSE. I AM THEREFORE CALLED VAASUDEVA. THAT WAS KALAYAVANA WHO WAS KILLED BY YOUR GLANCE. YOU HAVE LONG BEEN MY DEVOTEE. I CAME HERE TO GIVE YOU MY BLESSINGS.

MUCHUKUNDA WAS OVER-WHELMED WITH DEVOTION AND LOVE. HE BOWED RESPECTFULLY AT LORD KRISHNA'S FEET AND SOUGHT HIS BLESSINGS.

THUS ENDS THE FIFTH SESSION OF OUR RENDERING OF THE TENTH CHAPTER OF THE BHAGAWAT PURANA.

KRISHNA: THE ENCHANTER

PAREEKSHIT INTERRUPTED THE NARRATION OF SHUKADEVA.

WHAT HAPPENED TO MATHURA WHICH WAS BESIEGED BY THE ASURA ARMY, WHILE KRISHNA LED KALAYAVANA TO HIS DEATH?

BALARAMA AND HIS ARMY TRIED THEIR BEST TO FIGHT THE ASURA ARMY OF KALAYAVANA.

"WHEN KRISHNA RETURNED TO MATHURA HE AND BALARAMA DECIMATED THE ENTIRE ARMY OF KALAYAVANA.

"ON KRISHNA'S BIDDING, THE YADAVA SOLDIERS TOOK ALL THE PRECIOUS OBJECTS BELONGING TO THE DEFEATED ARMY.

TAKE ALL THEIR TREASURE AND JEWELS. LET THEM BE BROUGHT TO DWARAKA.

"JUST AS THE OXEN LADEN WITH THE TREASURE WERE BEING LED AWAY —

MY LORD! JARASANDHA IS APPROACHING MATHURA AGAIN. FOR THE EIGHTEENTH TIME! HIS ARMY HAS REACHED THE CITY GATES.

"SEVENTEEN TIMES JARASANDHA HAD ATTACKED MATHURA AND SEVENTEEN TIMES KRISHNA AND BALARAMA HAD DRIVEN HIM AWAY. BUT ON THIS OCCASION KRISHNA THOUGHT OF A DIFFERENT PLAN.

BALARAMA! PRETEND YOU ARE AFRAID.

AMAR CHITRA KATHA

BUT I AM NOT AFRAID, KRISHNA!

OF COURSE I KNOW YOU ARE NOT. BUT PRETEND ANYWAY. LET US RUN.

"WHEN JARASANDHA AND HIS ARMY ENTERED MATHURA, HE COULD NOT BELIEVE WHAT HE SAW.

HA! HA! HA! LOOK AT THEM RUN! THEY ARE SCARED OF ME.

"HE SAID TO HIS MEN —

LET'S FOLLOW THEM. QUICK!

"ALTHOUGH THEY WERE ON FOOT, KRISHNA AND BALARAMA HAD A GOOD LEAD.

HURRY! WE MUST CATCH UP WITH THEM. THEY ARE NOT EVEN ARMED. WE CAN FINISH THEM OFF EASILY.

"BY NOW KRISHNA AND BALARAMA HAD REACHED THE FOOT OF A HIGH HILL CALLED PRAVARSHANA.

LET'S GO UP! IT'S QUITE STEEP AND SLIPPERY. THEY WON'T BE ABLE TO FOLLOW US ON THEIR CHARIOTS.

YES, IT NEVER STOPS RAINING ON MOUNT PRAVARSHANA.

"JARASANDHA WAS FURIOUS.

SET FIRE TO THE MOUNTAIN FROM ALL SIDES. DON'T LET THEM ESCAPE ALIVE.

"SOON ANGRY FLAMES SURROUNDED THE MOUNTAIN. THE TWO BROTHERS MADE A DARING DECISION.

LET'S JUMP DOWN.

YES, THE SMOKE AND FIRE WILL GIVE US A COVER.

"WITH A HUGE LEAP, THEY REACHED THE FOOT OF THE HILL.

JARASANDHA AND HIS MEN ARE LOOKING FOR US ON THE SLOPES. LET'S RUN!

"KRISHNA AND BALARAMA THEN SWIFTLY MADE THEIR WAY TO DWARAKA.

"JARASANDHA WAS CONVINCED HE HAD DESTROYED HIS ENEMY.

AT LAST! KRISHNA AND BALARAMA HAVE BEEN BURNT TO DEATH IN THAT FIRE. I CAN NOW GO BACK TO MAGADHA IN PEACE.

"IN DUE TIME BALARAMA WAS MARRIED TO KING RAIVATA'S DAUGHTER REVATI.

"KRISHNA HAD SET HIS HEART ON RUKMINI, THE LOVELY DAUGHTER OF BHEESHMAKA, KING OF VIDARBHA.

RUKMINI HAS BEAUTY, INTELLIGENCE AND GRACE. SHE WILL BE THE IDEAL WIFE FOR ME.

"SINCE THE TIME SHE WAS A LITTLE GIRL, RUKMINI HAD HEARD OF THE EXPLOITS OF KRISHNA.

EVERYONE PRAISES HIS GOOD LOOKS, VALOUR AND VIRTUES. HE IS THE ONE I WILL MARRY.

"RUKMINI HAD FIVE BROTHERS — RUKMI, RUKMARATHA, RUKMABAHU, RUKMAKESHA AND RUKMAMALI.

WE SHOULD LOOK FOR A SUITABLE GROOM FOR RUKMINI.

WHY NOT KRISHNA?

NO, NEVER! I SHALL NOT ALLOW HER TO MARRY KRISHNA

IT WAS RUKMI THE ELDEST WHO PROTESTED.

RUKMINI WILL BE MARRIED TO MY FRIEND SHISHUPALA.

"RUKMINI WAS HEARTBROKEN.

MARRY SHISHUPALA! THAT PRINCE OF CHEDI! I CANNOT EVEN THINK OF IT!

"SHE WAS PLUNGED IN GLOOM FOR A WHILE.

WHAT SHOULD I DO? I FEEL SO CONFUSED.

"SHE THOUGHT OF A WAY OUT AND SENT FOR AN OLD TRUSTED BRAHMIN.

WILL YOU TAKE A MESSAGE TO SHRI KRISHNA?

CERTAINLY, MY CHILD.

"THE OLD BRAHMIN SET OUT FOR DWARAKA AT ONCE. ON REACHING THE ROYAL PALACE HE BEHELD KRISHNA SEATED ON A GOLDEN THRONE.

"KRISHNA RECEIVED THE BRAHMIN WITH DUE RESPECT.

WELCOME TO DWARAKA, O VENERABLE ONE.

"AFTER THE BRAHMIN HAD BEEN FED AND REFRESHED, KRISHNA ASKED HIM THE PURPOSE OF HIS VISIT.

I HAVE COME WITH A MESSAGE FROM PRINCESS RUKMINI.

"THE BRAHMIN DUTIFULLY REPEATED THE LONG MESSAGE GIVEN BY RUKMINI.

O KRISHNA, WITH YOUR HANDSOME LOOKS, NOBLE NATURE AND WISDOM, YOU ARE TRULY UN-MATCHED.

I HAVE CHOSEN YOU FOR MY HUSBAND. HONOUR ME BY COMING HERE AND ACCEPTING ME AS YOUR WIFE.

MY BROTHER RUKMI HAS ARRANGED MY MARRIAGE WITH SHISHUPALA, BUT THE VERY IDEA OF BEING ANY-ONE ELSE'S WIFE IS UNTHINKABLE.

I SUGGEST THAT YOU COME TO VIDARBHA THE DAY BEFORE THE WEDDING AND TAKE ME AWAY FORCIBLY*.

IT IS CUSTOMARY FOR THE BRIDE-TO-BE TO VISIT THE TEMPLE OF PARVATI OUTSIDE THE TOWN A DAY BEFORE THE WEDDING CEREMONY. THAT'S WHERE YOU WILL BE ABLE TO MEET ME.

"KRISHNA CONFESSED—

I TOO HAVE LOST MY HEART TO RUKMINI. SO REST ASSURED, I WILL SURELY RESCUE HER FROM MY OPPONENTS.

BUT THERE'S NO TIME TO LOSE. I MUST CALL MY CHARIOTEER.

DARUKA! DARUKA!

* SUCH A MARRIAGE WAS CALLED 'RAKSHASA VIVAHA' AND HAD SOCIAL SANCTION.

HURRY UP AND PREPARE TO LEAVE FOR VIDARBHA. WE HAVE TO REACH THERE BEFORE NIGHTFALL DAY AFTER TOMORROW.

I'LL BE READY AT ONCE.

"WITH KRISHNA AND THE VENERABLE BRAHMIN ON THE CHARIOT, DARUKA DROVE FAST IN THE NIGHT.

COME ON! MY PETS! GALLOP AS FAST AS YOU CAN TO VIDARBHA.

"KUNDINAPURA, THE CAPITAL OF VIDARBHA BORE A FESTIVE LOOK. THE STREETS HAD BEEN CLEANED. COLOURFUL BUNTING AND BANNERS FLUTTERED IN THE BREEZE.

"PEOPLE BEDECKED THEMSELVES WITH FLOWERS, ORNAMENTS AND BRIGHT NEW CLOTHES. THE AROMA OF INCENSE PERVADED THE AIR AS THE BRAHMINS CHANTED HYMNS FROM THE VEDAS.

"AFTER A CEREMONIAL BATH, RUKMINI WAS DRESSED IN NEW CLOTHES AND GLITTERING ORNAMENTS.

YOU LOOK SO BEAUTIFUL. LET ME TIE THIS AUSPICIOUS THREAD ON YOUR WRIST.

"MEANWHILE, TRADITIONAL RITES WERE ALSO PERFORMED ON THE BRIDEGROOM, SHISHUPALA.

"ACCOMPANIED BY A LARGE ARMY OF DECORATED CHARIOTS, ELEPHANTS, HORSES AND SOLDIERS, THE GROOM'S PARTY REACHED KUNDINAPURA.

"BHEESHMAKA WELCOMED THEM WITH DUE HONOUR AND LED THEM TO THEIR APPOINTED PALACES.

"WITH SHISHUPALA CAME JARASANDHA, DANTAVAKRA, VIDURATHA AND PAUNDRAKA, ALL OF WHOM, AS ALLIES OF SHISHUPALA, HATED KRISHNA.

WE MUST MAKE SURE THAT SHISHUPALA MARRIES RUKMINI.

MY ARMY WILL SOON REACH HERE.

WE TOO HAVE BROUGHT OUR ARMIES.

IF THAT KRISHNA PROVES AN OBSTACLE TO THIS MARRIAGE, WE ARE PREPARED TO FIGHT HIM.

HE WON'T HAVE A CHANCE AGAINST OUR COMBINED FORCES.

"MEANWHILE AT DWARAKA, BALARAMA HEARD OF THESE PLANS.

ALL THESE KINGS ARE PREPARED FOR BATTLE AND KRISHNA HAS GONE ALONE!

"AS HE HURRIEDLY GATHERED HIS ARMY AND SET OUT FOR KUNDINAPURA, HIS HEART WAS FILLED WITH CONCERN.

I KNOW I SHOULD NOT WORRY. KRISHNA IS MORE THAN A MATCH FOR ALL OF THEM.

BUT THERE'S BOUND TO BE A BIG FIGHT AND I MUST BE BY KRISHNA'S SIDE.

"BY NOW RUKMINI WAS SICK WITH WORRY.

HERE I AM WAITING FOR LORD KRISHNA, BUT EVEN THE VENERABLE BRAHMIN HAS NOT YET RETURNED.

I WONDER WHAT HAS HAPPENED?

PERHAPS LORD KRISHNA DID NOT FIND ME WORTHY OF HIM.

"IN HER SORROW RUKMINI REMAINED WITH HER EYES CLOSED.

"WHEN SHE OPENED HER EYES, SHE CAUGHT SIGHT OF THE OLD BRAHMIN.

AH THERE HE IS! HE LOOKS CALM AND HAPPY.

"SHE HURRIED UP TO HIM.

DARE I HOPE..?

YES, KRISHNA IS HERE.

AND WHAT'S MORE, HE HAS VOWED TO TAKE YOU AWAY.

"RUKMINI'S HEART OVERFLOWED WITH HAPPINESS.

HOW CAN I EVER HOPE TO REPAY YOU FOR WHAT YOU HAVE DONE FOR ME. I CAN ONLY BOW TO YOU.

"THE NEWS OF KRISHNA'S ARRIVAL REACHED BHEESHMAKA.

THE TWO YADAVA BROTHERS ARE HERE! PERHAPS TO WITNESS RUKMINI'S WEDDING.

LET A PALACE BE PREPARED FOR THEIR STAY. TELL THE MUSICIANS TO FOLLOW ME.

I WILL WELCOME THEM MYSELF.

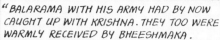

"BALARAMA WITH HIS ARMY HAD BY NOW CAUGHT UP WITH KRISHNA. THEY TOO WERE WARMLY RECEIVED BY BHEESHMAKA.

WE ARE HONOURED BY YOUR PRESENCE ON THIS OCCASION.

"THE NEWS OF KRISHNA'S ARRIVAL SPREAD QUICKLY.

HAVE YOU HEARD? KRISHNA HAS COME TO OUR TOWN!

LET'S GO AND SEE HIM.

"THEY THRONGED THE PALACE WHERE KRISHNA WAS STAYING.

OUR PRINCESS RUKMINI WOULD MAKE HIM AN IDEAL WIFE.

SHE CERTAINLY WOULD!

LET'S HOPE AND PRAY THAT KRISHNA TAKES RUKMINI'S HAND IN MARRIAGE.

"JUST THEN —

AH! THERE SHE IS. PRINCESS RUKMINI!

HOW LOVELY SHE LOOKS.

"FOLLOWED BY A GROUP OF SOLDIERS, RUKMINI MADE HER WAY TO THE TEMPLE OF GODDESS PARVATI.

"SHE SEEMED LOST IN THOUGHT AS SHE WALKED ALONG WITH HER ATTENDANTS AND RELATIVES.

WILL HE COME? DARE I HOPE?

"THE OLDER WOMEN GUIDED HER IN THE RITUALS.

BOW TO LORD SHIVA AND PARVATI AND ASK FOR THEIR BLESSINGS.

"IN A SOFT VOICE, RUKMINI SAID—

O GODDESS PARVATI, I PRAY TO YOU. GRANT MY HEART'S DESIRE. LET KRISHNA BECOME MY HUSBAND.

"DEVOTEDLY RUKMINI WORSHIPPED THE GODDESS, WITH OFFERINGS OF SANDAL-PASTE, GARLANDS, FRUITS AND SWEETS. THEN SHE STEPPED OUT OF THE TEMPLE.

"WHEN THE KINGS ASSEMBLED IN THE CITY BEHELD HER BEAUTIFUL FORM AS SHE EMERGED FROM THE TEMPLE, THEY STOOD ENRAPTURED.

"BUT IGNORING THEIR AMAZED LOOKS, RUKMINI WALKED ON, GENTLY LIFTING THE TRESSES FALLING ON HER PRETTY FACE. SHE LOOKED UP AT LAST...

...AND HER GAZE FELL DIRECTLY ON KRISHNA.

"BEBORE ANY ONE KNEW WHAT WAS HAPPENING, KRISHNA REACHED WHERE RUKMINI STOOD.

"AND LIFTING HER UP, PLACED HER ON HIS CHARIOT.

"LIKE A LION TAKING AWAY HIS SHARE FROM THE SURROUNDING JACKALS, KRISHNA SPED AWAY WITH RUKMINI.

"BALARAMA AND HIS ARMY FOLLOWED THEM SWIFTLY.

"WHEN JARASANDHA AND THE OTHER KINGS RECOVERED FROM THE SHOCK OF THE QUICK PACE OF EVENTS, THEY CRIED —

FIE ON US! WE WERE LEFT HOLDING OUR BOWS WHILE THAT COWHERD WOUNDED OUR PRIDE AND WENT AWAY WITH RUKMINI.

COME, DON YOUR ARMOUR.

"THE KINGS AND THEIR ARMIES FOLLOWED KRISHNA'S TRAIL, WITH THEIR BOWS STRUNG IN READINESS.

"SKILLED AS THEY WERE IN ARCHERY, JARASANDHA'S SOLDIERS SOON COVERED KRISHNA'S ARMY WITH A SHOWER OF ARROWS.

"THE SOLDIERS OF BALARAMA'S ARMY VALIANTLY RESPONDED TO THE ATTACK.

"RUKMINI TURNED TO KRISHNA WITH HER BEAUTIFUL EYES WIDENED IN FEAR.

DON'T BE AFRAID, O BEAUTIFUL ONE! JUST WATCH HOW YOUR ARMY DESTROYS THE ENEMIES.

"TRUE TO KRISHNA'S WORDS, THE YADAVA ARMY CHIEFS LIKE GADA AND BALARAMA ANNIHILATED THEIR FOES. SOON THE PATH WAS STREWN WITH FALLEN HORSES, ELEPHANTS AND BROKEN CHARIOTS.

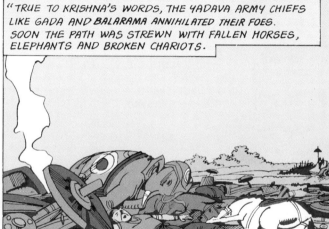

"THE SIGHT OF SO MANY OF THEIR SOLDIERS SLAIN IN BATTLE PUT FEAR INTO THE HEARTS OF THEIR KINGS. JARASANDHA AND HIS ALLIES FLED.

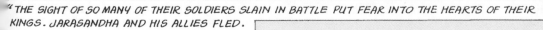

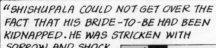

"SHISHUPALA COULD NOT GET OVER THE FACT THAT HIS BRIDE-TO-BE HAD BEEN KIDNAPPED. HE WAS STRICKEN WITH SORROW AND SHOCK."

"JARASANDHA TRIED TO CONSOLE HIM."

GET OVER YOUR GRIEF, O SHISHUPALA. WE CANNOT ALWAYS HAVE WHAT WE WISH FOR.

LOOK AT ME! SEVENTEEN TIMES WAS I DEFEATED IN BATTLE BY KRISHNA, LOSING 23 AKSHAUHINIS EACH TIME. BUT, FINALLY, IN MY EIGHTEENTH ATTEMPT, I SUCCEEDED.

GRANTED THAT TODAY A SMALL ARMY OF KRISHNA HAS ROUTED OUR MIGHTY COMBINED FORCE, BUT SOON LUCK WILL BE ON OUR SIDE.

PERHAPS YOU ARE RIGHT.

"THUS CONSOLED BY HIS FRIENDS, SHISHUPALA RETURNED TO HIS CAPITAL. BUT RUKMI'S ANGER KNEW NO BOUNDS."

HOW DARE HE TAKE AWAY MY SISTER!

"HE PUT ON HIS ARMOUR AND GATHERED HIS WEAPONS TO FOLLOW KRISHNA."

I VOW THAT I SHALL NOT RETURN TILL I KILL KRISHNA AND RESCUE RUKMINI.

"JUMPING ON TO HIS CHARIOT HE SAID —

LET MY ARMY FOLLOW ME. TAKE MY CHARIOT WHEREVER KRISHNA IS. TODAY I WILL CRUSH THE PRIDE OF THAT COWHERD.

"UNAWARE OF THE DIVINE POWERS OF KRISHNA, RUKMI SPED AHEAD OF HIS ARMY TO CONFRONT KRISHNA ALONE.

WAIT A MINUTE, YOU BLACK SHEEP OF THE YADAVA RACE.

BEFORE MY ARROWS KILL YOU, LEAVE THAT INNOCENT YOUNG GIRL ALONE AND RUN FOR YOUR LIFE.

"KRISHNA MERELY SMILED IN REPLY. WITH A SERIES OF WELL-AIMED ARROWS, HE KILLED RUKMI'S HORSES AND CHARIOTEER AND BROKE HIS BOW.

"RUKMI PICKED UP BOW AFTER BOW, ONLY TO HAVE THEM BROKEN BY KRISHNA'S SHARP ARROWS. HE THEN TRIED OTHER WEAPONS— THE MACE, THE JAVELIN, THE SHAKTI* AND THE SHIELD.

"BUT KRISHNA DESTROYED ALL OF THEM WITH EASE. RUKMI'S ANGER AND FRUSTRATION KNEW NO BOUNDS.

* A POWERFUL WEAPON.

"SWORD IN HAND, RUKMI JUMPED DOWN FROM HIS CHARIOT AND CHARGED AT KRISHNA, LIKE A MOTH FLYING TOWARDS A FLAME.

"BUT KRISHNA'S ARROWS REDUCED HIS SWORD AND SHIELD TO PIECES.

"WHEN KRISHNA TOOK UP HIS OWN SWORD AND ADVANCED TOWARDS RUKMI—

O LORD OF THE UNIVERSE, YOU ARE THE MOST POWERFUL OF ALL- BUT YOU ARE BENEVOLENT TOO. IT DOES NOT BEFIT YOU TO KILL MY BROTHER.

"RUKMINI'S VOICE WAS CHOKED WITH EMOTION AND SHE WAS TREMBLING WITH FEAR.

HOW SCARED SHE LOOKS, THE POOR DEAR.

FOR HER SAKE, I'LL SPARE HIS LIFE BUT I MUST TEACH HIM A LESSON.

"FIRST KRISHNA TIED RUKMI UP.

"WITH HIS SWORD KRISHNA SHAVED OFF PATCHES OF HAIR FROM RUKMI'S HEAD AND MOUSTACHE.

"BY THEN, BALARAMA AND THE YADAVA ARMY ARRIVED ON THE SCENE, AFTER HAVING DESTROYED RUKMI'S SOLDIERS. BALARAMA WAS SHOCKED TO SEE RUKMI'S DISFIGURED STATE.

KRISHNA! WHAT HAVE YOU DONE?

DISFIGURING A RELATIVE IS AS BAD AS KILLING HIM.

"ADDRESSING RUKMINI, BALARAMA SAID —

NOBLE ONE, DON'T THINK ILL OF US BECAUSE OF WHAT HAPPENED. YOUR BROTHER SUFFERED AS A RESULT OF HIS OWN DEEDS.

ALAS! THE DHARMA OF THE KSHATRIYAS* IS SUCH THAT A MAN MAY KILL HIS OWN BROTHER IN WAR.

YET IT IS NOBLE, KRISHNA, TO FORGIVE THE WORST ACT OF YOUR RELATIVES. LET HIM GO; DON'T KILL HIM. HIS OWN GUILT WILL DESTROY HIM.

THOSE BELONGING TO THE WARRIOR CASTE.

" TO CONSOLE RUKMINI HE SAID —

IT IS FOR HIS OWN GOOD THAT YOUR BROTHER HAS BEEN PUNISHED.

"RUKMI COULD NOT GET OVER HIS HUMILIATION.

HOW CAN I RETURN TO MY CAPITAL IN THIS STATE? I WILL HAVE TO FIND ANOTHER PLACE TO LIVE.

"RUKMI BUILT A CITY WHICH HE NAMED BHOJKAT.

I SHALL NOT ENTER KUNDINAPURA TILL I SLAY THAT WICKED KRISHNA AND RESCUE MY LITTLE SISTER.

"AFTER REACHING DWARAKA THE FORMAL WEDDING CEREMONY OF KRISHNA AND RUKMINI WAS PERFORMED WITH DUE POMP.

THE CITIZENS OF DWARAKA WERE EXCEEDINGLY HAPPY TO WITNESS THE WEDDING OF KRISHNA AND RUKMINI. IN DUE COURSE, A SON WAS BORN TO THE COUPLE. THEY NAMED HIM PRADYUMNA.

"PRADYUMNA WAS VERY GOOD-LOOKING AND WAS IN FACT AN INCARNATION OF KAMADEVA, THE GOD OF LOVE.

"WHEN PRADYUMNA WAS JUST TEN DAYS OLD, A DEMON NAMED SHAMBARASURA KIDNAPPED HIM.

"THE WICKED DEMON THREW PRADYUMNA INTO THE SEA.

HE WAS DESTINED TO BE MY FOE! I MUST GET RID OF HIM.

"A HUGE FISH SWALLOWED THE TINY BABY. BUT SOON—

WHAT A FINE FISH! I WILL PRESENT IT TO OUR KING SHAMBARASURA.

"WHEN SHAMBARASURA'S COOK CUT OPEN THE BIG FISH, HE WAS ASTONISHED.

SEE! THERE'S AN INFANT INSIDE THE FISH. LET'S GIVE THE BABY TO MAYAVATI, THE KING'S MAID.

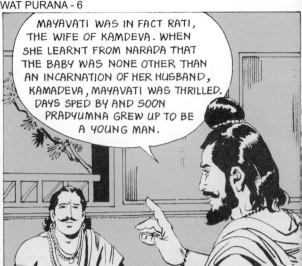

MAYAVATI WAS IN FACT RATI, THE WIFE OF KAMDEVA. WHEN SHE LEARNT FROM NARADA THAT THE BABY WAS NONE OTHER THAN AN INCARNATION OF HER HUSBAND, KAMADEVA, MAYAVATI WAS THRILLED. DAYS SPED BY AND SOON PRADYUMNA GREW UP TO BE A YOUNG MAN.

"MAYAVATI NARRATED THE STORY OF HIS BIRTH TO PRADYUMNA.

SO YOU WILL HAVE TO CONFRONT THE ASURA. I WILL TEACH YOU MAHA* MAYA+ BY WHICH YOU CAN DEFEAT HIM.

"AS ADVISED BY MAYAVATI, PRADYUMNA PURPOSELY PICKED UP A FIGHT WITH SHAMBARASURA.

HOW DARE YOU TALK TO ME LIKE THAT! JUST WAIT!

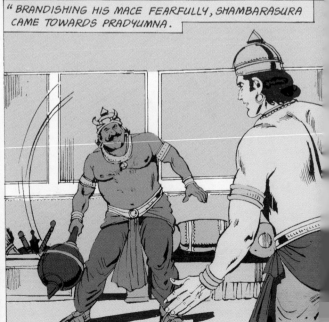

" BRANDISHING HIS MACE FEARFULLY, SHAMBARASURA CAME TOWARDS PRADYUMNA.

* GREAT   + ILLUSORY POWERS.

"BUT PRADYUMNA WAS MORE THAN READY. WITH A SINGLE BLOW, HE FELLED THE DEMON'S MACE.

I'LL HAVE TO USE MAYA.

"SHAMBARASURA ROSE RAPIDLY IN THE AIR AND BEGAN TO RAIN WEAPONS DOWN ON PRADYUMNA.

HE IS TRYING TO CREATE ALL SORTS OF CREATURES TO SCARE ME. I'LL HAVE TO USE THE ART MAYAVATI TAUGHT ME.

"WITH THE HELP OF MAHA-MAYA, PRADYUMNA COULD COUNTER ALL THE WICKED MOVES OF THE ASURA. FINALLY HE TOOK UP A SHARP SWORD...

"...AND CUT OFF SHAMBARASURA'S HEAD.

"MAYAVATI TOOK PRADYUMNA TO DWARAKA.

"SHE LED THE BRAVE PRADYUMNA TO KRISHNA'S PALACE.

SEE THAT HANDSOME MAN. HE LOOKS SO MUCH LIKE KRISHNA.

HIS DARK LOOKS CONTRAST SO WELL WITH HER FAIR FACE.

"JUST THEN, RUKMINI ARRIVED.

WHO IS THIS YOUNG MAN, I WONDER?

HAD MY SON SURVIVED, HE TOO WOULD HAVE BEEN HIS AGE.

"RUKMINI TOO NOTICED PRADYUMNA'S RESEMBLANCE TO KRISHNA.

"KRISHNA TOO CAME ON THE SCENE BUT STOOD BY SILENTLY, AS IF HE KNEW NOTHING. THEN NARADA ARRIVED THERE AND NARRATED THE PAST EVENTS.

HE IS YOUR SON, RUKMINI, WHO WAS LOST WHEN HE WAS AN INFANT.

HOW LUCKY WE ARE TO HAVE HIM BACK.

AS IF HE'S BACK FROM THE DEAD.

SHUKADEVA THEN NARRATED THE STORY OF KRISHNA'S MARRIAGE TO JAMBAVATI AND SATYABHAMA.

SATRAJIT HAD ONCE FALSELY BLAMED KRISHNA AND TO ATONE FOR HIS CRIME, HE GAVE HIS DAUGHTER SATYABHAMA IN MARRIAGE TO KRISHNA ALONG WITH THE SYAMANTAKA GEM.

PAREEKSHIT INTERRUPTED THE NARRATION.

NO, NO, TELL ME EVERYTHING IN DETAIL. WHO WAS SATRAJIT? WHAT WAS SATRAJIT'S CRIME? WHERE DID HE GET THE GEM? WHY DID HE MARRY HIS DAUGHTER TO KRISHNA?

"IN DWARAKA THERE LIVED SATRAJIT WHO WAS A GREAT DEVOTEE OF SURYA, THE SUN GOD. ONE DAY SURYA APPEARED BEFORE HIM.

I AM PLEASED WITH YOUR DEVOTION. TAKE THIS SYAMANTAKA GEM.

"WHEN SATRAJIT WORE THE JEWEL ON HIS NECK, HE LOOKED AS RESPLENDENT AS THE SUN. WHEN HE ENTERED THE CITY —

WHAT IS THAT STRANGE GLARE? I CAN'T OPEN MY EYES!

HAS THE SUN COME DOWN TO EARTH?

LET'S GO AND TELL KRISHNA.

"THEY FOUND KRISHNA PLAYING DICE.

KRISHNA! O KRISHNA! SEE LORD SURYA IS HERE!

PERHAPS HE IS LOOKING FOR YOU.

"KRISHNA LAUGHED AND SAID —

OH THAT! IT'S NOT THE SUN. THAT'S SATRAJIT WEARING A BRILLIANT JEWEL.

"AFTER DISPLAYING THE SYAMANTAKA GEM TO HIS PEOPLE, SATRAJIT HAD IT INSTALLED IN A SMALL PRAYER ROOM.

"SOON THE FAME OF THE GEM BEGAN TO SPREAD.

THE SYAMANTAKA IS A FABULOUS GEM. IT YIELDS EIGHT MEASURES OF GOLD EVERY DAY.

WHAT'S MORE, THE GEM PROTECTS THE PEOPLE AROUND FROM DISEASE AND FAMINE.

"ONE DAY KRISHNA VISITED SATRAJIT.

EVERYONE IN DWARAKA IS TALKING ABOUT YOUR FANTASTIC GEM.

YES, IT IS INDEED EXTRAORDINARY.

NOW THAT YOU HAVE ENOUGH GOLD, WHY DON'T YOU GIVE THE GEM TO OUR KING, UGRASENA?

WHY SHOULD I? IT BELONGS TO ME.

"THOUGH HE REFUSED TO GIVE IT TO THE KING, SATRAJIT GAVE THE GEM TO HIS BROTHER PRASENA.

I'LL KEEP IT JUST FOR A DAY.

BE CAREFUL WHILE YOU GO HUNTING.

"WHILE HE WAS OUT HUNTING, PRASENA WAS KILLED BY A LION.

"THE LION WAS FASCINATED BY THE BRILLIANCE OF THE GEM AND TOOK IT AWAY TO HIS DEN. JUST THEN——

"IT WAS JAMBAVAN, THE BEAR WHO HAD ATTACKED THE LION. JAMBAVAN GAVE THE GEM TO HIS LITTLE SON TO PLAY WITH.

"MEANWHILE IN DWARAKA, SATRAJIT WAS GETTING ANXIOUS ABOUT HIS BROTHER.

PRASENA HASN'T RETURNED. PERHAPS KRISHNA HAS KILLED HIM FOR THE SAKE OF THE SYAMANTAKA GEM.

"SATRAJIT'S WORDS OF ACCUSATION TRAVELLED FROM MOUTH TO MOUTH.

SATRAJIT IS BLAMING KRISHNA

HE SAYS KRISHNA COVETED THE GEM.

"KRISHNA TOO HEARD OF IT.

I MUST CLEAR MY NAME.

"HE CONFIDED IN SOME OF HIS FRIENDS.

COME WITH ME TO THE FOREST. WE WILL FIND OUT WHAT REALLY HAPPENED TO PRASENA.

"SOON KRISHNA AND HIS COMPANIONS FOUND THE BODIES OF PRASENA AND HIS HORSE.

SEE! PRASENA AND HIS HORSE MUST HAVE BEEN ATTACKED AND KILLED BY A LION.

LET'S FOLLOW THE LION'S TRAIL.

"FOLLOWING THE LION'S TRACK THEY REACHED A CAVE ON THE MOUNTAIN SIDE.

THE LION TOO HAS BEEN KILLED.

AND HERE IS THE TRACK OF A BEAR LEADING INTO THE DEN.

"KRISHNA SAID—

I'LL GO IN ALONE. YOU WAIT OUTSIDE THE CAVE.

AS YOU WISH.

"WHEN HE ENTERED THE DARK CAVE—

WHY, THE BEAR'S CUBS ARE PLAYING WITH THE GEM AS IF IT WERE A TOY.

"QUIETLY KRISHNA APPROACHED THE CUBS; BUT THE MOTHER SENSED HIS PRESENCE.

AEEE!

"HER CRY BROUGHT JAMBAVAN THERE AND HE ANGRILY ATTACKED KRISHNA.

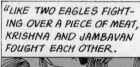

"LIKE TWO EAGLES FIGHTING OVER A PIECE OF MEAT, KRISHNA AND JAMBAVAN FOUGHT EACH OTHER.

"THEY FOUGHT WITH ROCKS AND WITH TREE TRUNKS.

"THEN THEY WRESTLED WITH EACH OTHER. BUT SO STRONG AND WELL-MATCHED WERE THE TWO THAT THE FIGHT WENT ON AND ON.

"KRISHNA'S COMPANIONS NOW BEGAN TO LOSE PATIENCE.

IT IS TWELVE DAYS SINCE KRISHNA WENT INSIDE.

THERE IS NO USE WAITING ANY MORE.

LET'S GO AND GIVE THE SAD NEWS TO DWARAKA.

"MEANWHILE, INSIDE THE CAVE JAMBAVAN MET HIS MATCH IN KRISHNA. AFTER 28 DAYS' CONTINUOUS FIGHT—

LORD! I KNOW WHO YOU ARE.

"KRISHNA AFFECTIONATELY PATTED JAMBAVAN AND SAID—

I CAME HERE IN SEARCH OF THE SYAMANTAKA GEM. I NEED IT TO PROVE MY INNOCENCE.

MOST HAPPILY I'LL GIVE YOU NOT ONLY THE GEM BUT ALSO MY DAUGHTER JAMBAVATI.

"KRISHNA RETURNED TO DWARAKA WITH THE GEM AND JAMBAVATI.

KRISHNA IS BACK. KRISHNA IS HERE.

WITH THE GEM AROUND HIS NECK AND A BEAUTIFUL MAIDEN WITH HIM.

"KRISHNA SUMMONED SATRAJIT TO KING UGRASENA'S COURT—

IN THE PRESENCE OF THIS GATHERING, I WANT TO RELATE HOW THE GEM CAME TO BE IN MY POSSESSION.

"SATRAJIT FELT TERRIBLY EMBARRASSED WHEN HE HEARD THE WHOLE STORY. WITH HIS HEAD HUNG LOW, HE MEEKLY ACCEPTED THE GEM BACK ON KRISHNA'S INSISTENCE.

HOW BAD OF ME TO HAVE ACCUSED KRISHNA.

"SATRAJIT WAS UNHAPPY AND WORRIED.

WHAT SHOULD I DO TO ATONE FOR MY WRONG? HOW CAN I PLEASE KRISHNA NOW?

"AT LAST HE DECIDED —

MY LOVE FOR THE JEWEL MADE ME MALIGN HIM. NOW I'LL GIVE MY JEWEL-LIKE DAUGHTER TO KRISHNA IN MARRIAGE.

I OFFER YOU MY DAUGHTER SATYA-BHAMA AS WELL AS THE SYAMANTAKA GEM.

"KRISHNA ACCEPTED SATYABHAMA AND MARRIED HER WITH DUE CEREMONY.

I CANNOT ACCEPT THE GEM. LET IT REMAIN WITH YOU AS A GIFT OF SURYA. HOWEVER IF YOU WISH, YOU MAY GIVE US THE GOLD PRODUCED FROM IT.

"SATYABHAMA WAS VERY BEAUTIFUL AND MANY A YOUNG MAN OF DWARAKA HAD HOPED TO MARRY HER. AMONG THEM WERE AKRURA AND KRITAVARMA.

SATRAJIT HAD PROMISED TO MARRY SATYA-BHAMA TO ONE OF US.

AND NOW HE'S MARRIED HER TO KRISHNA.

WE MUST TAKE REVENGE.

"THEY WENT TO SHATADHANVA, ANOTHER YADAVA, WHO HAD HOPED FOR SATYABHAMA'S HAND.

WHY DON'T YOU KILL SATRAJIT AND TAKE AWAY THE SYAMANTAKA GEM?

"SHATADHANVA AGREED. IN THE DEAD OF THE NIGHT HE WENT TO SATRAJIT'S HOUSE. NEXT MORNING —

OH! MY POOR FATHER HAS BEEN KILLED! THE GEM HAS BEEN STOLEN!

"MEANWHILE KRISHNA AND BALARAMA HAD GONE TO HASTINAPURA. SATYABHAMA FOLLOWED THEM THERE.

I FEEL SO HELPLESS AND ALONE.

DON'T WORRY. WE WILL GO TO DWARAKA AND FIND THE KILLER AND THE GEM.

"SHATADHANVA WAS SCARED TO HEAR OF KRISHNA'S RETURN. HE RAN FOR HELP TO KRITAVARMA.

HELP ME! SAVE ME FROM KRISHNA.

NO! I WILL NOT CONFRONT KRISHNA.

"WHEN KRITAVARMA REFUSED TO HELP, SHATADHANVA PLEADED WITH AKRURA, BUT IN VAIN.

NO! WHO WOULD DARE TO FACE KRISHNA WHO PLAYFULLY HELD MOUNT GOVARDHANA ON HIS HAND FOR SEVEN DAYS. NOT ME!

THEN I MUST FLEE! AT LEAST KEEP THIS GEM WITH YOU.

"SHATADHANVA SPED AWAY ON HORSEBACK. BUT SOON KRISHNA AND BALARAMA WERE ON HIS TRAIL.

THERE HE IS! HE'S JUMPED OFF FROM HIS HORSE.

LET'S RUN AFTER HIM.

"KRISHNA AND BALARAMA GOT DOWN FROM THE CHARIOT AND RAN AFTER SHATADHANVA. KRISHNA AIMED HIS CHAKRA AT SHATADHANVA.

"BUT WHEN THEY SEARCHED HIM FOR THE GEM —

OH! HE DOESN'T HAVE THE GEM. WE NEED NOT HAVE KILLED HIM.

HE MUST HAVE GIVEN IT TO SOMEONE FOR SAFE KEEPING.

"KRISHNA RETURNED TO DWARAKA ALONE WHILE BALARAMA PAID A VISIT TO MITHILA. MEANWHILE AKRURA AND KRITAVARMA HAD LEFT THE TOWN.

KRISHNA HAS KILLED SHATADHANVA.

HE WILL COME AFTER US NOW. LET'S RUN AWAY.

"KRISHNA SENT FOR AKRURA.

UNCLE, I KNOW THAT SHATADHANVA LEFT THE GEM WITH YOU. RIGHTFULLY IT BELONGS TO SATRAJIT'S DESCENDANTS AND THERE-FORE TO MY SON.

HOWEVER YOU MAY KEEP THE SYAMAN-TAKA GEM. JUST ALLOW ME TO SHOW IT TO EVERYONE IN DWARAKA AND CLEAR MY NAME.

HERE, HAVE IT.

KRISHNA THEN SHOWED THE JEWEL TO THE PEOPLE OF DWARAKA. HAVING CLEARED ALL DOUBTS FROM THE MINDS OF THE PEOPLE, HE RETURNED THE GEM TO AKRURA.

THUS ENDS THE SIXTH SESSION OF OUR RENDERING OF THE TENTH CHAPTER OF THE BHAGAWAT PURANA.

KRISHNA: THE VICTORIOUS

SHUKADEVA WAS NARRATING TO PAREEKSHIT THE STORY OF KRISHNA'S VARIOUS MARRIAGES.

ACCOMPANIED BY SATYAKI AND OTHER YADAVAS, KRISHNA PAID A VISIT TO INDRAPRASTHA TO MEET THE PANDAVAS

MY DEAR KRISHNA!

WHAT A SURPRISE!

" KRISHNA BOWED RESPECTFULLY TO YUDHISHTHIRA AND BHEEMA, BLESSED NAKULA AND SAHADEVA AND THEN —

ARJUNA, MY DEAR!

" KUNTI COULD NOT CONTAIN HER TEARS OF JOY.

O KRISHNA, WE WERE DELIGHTED THAT YOU WERE CONCERNED ABOUT US AND SENT AKRURA TO ENQUIRE ABOUT OUR WELL-BEING.

I AM SO HAPPY THAT ALL OF YOU ESCAPED FROM THE BURNING HOUSE OF LAC*

AND WE ARE SO HAPPY TO HAVE YOU HERE!

YOU MUST STAY AWHILE!

* SEE ACK NO 343

"KRISHNA WAS PERSUADED TO STAY IN INDRAPRASTHA FOR THE FOUR MONTHS OF THE RAINY SEASON. ONE DAY—

AAH! THIS HUNT HAS MADE ME TIRED.

LET US REST AWHILE, ARJUNA.

" AS THEY REFRESHED THEMSELVES —

LOOK, KRISHNA!

GO AND FIND OUT WHO SHE IS.

WHO ARE YOU? WHERE HAVE YOU COME FROM?

I AM SURYA'S DAUGHTER. MY NAME IS KALINDI.

WHY ARE YOU DOING SUCH SEVERE PENANCE?

I WANT TO OBTAIN LORD VISHNU AS MY HUSBAND.

MY FATHER HAS BUILT A HOUSE FOR ME IN THIS RIVER. I HAVE VOWED TO REMAIN HERE UNTIL I BEHOLD KRISHNA.

"ARJUNA WENT BACK TO KRISHNA.

SHE IS DETERMINED TO MARRY YOU.

SO BE IT!

"TAKING KALINDI WITH THEM, THEY RETURNED TO YUDHISHTHIRA'S PALACE.

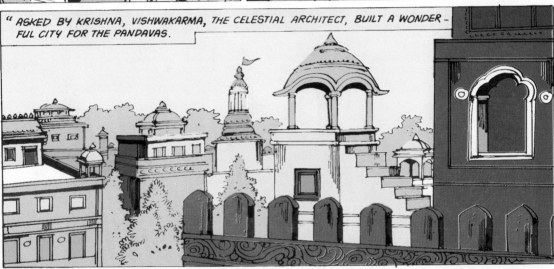

"ASKED BY KRISHNA, VISHWAKARMA, THE CELESTIAL ARCHITECT, BUILT A WONDERFUL CITY FOR THE PANDAVAS.

"LATER WITH THE HELP OF KRISHNA AND ARJUNA, AGNI, THE GOD OF FIRE, DEVOURED THE KHANDAVA FOREST. BUT WHEN THE FOREST WAS BEING CONSUMED BY AGNI, ARJUNA SAVED MAYA THE DEMON.

"THE GRATEFUL MAYA BUILT A BEAUTIFUL HALL FOR YUDHISHTHIRA AT INDRAPRASTHA.

"THEN ONE DAY —

I HAVE SPENT FOUR MONTHS IN YOUR DELIGHTFUL COMPANY. NOW I MUST RETURN.

"AFTER REACHING DWARAKA KRISHNA MARRIED KALINDI ON AN AUSPICIOUS DAY.

"MITRAVINDA, THE PRINCESS OF UJJAYINI, HAD SET HER HEART ON KRISHNA.

I WILL MARRY ONLY KRISHNA.

"HER BROTHERS WERE ALLIES OF DURYODHANA.

NO, WE CANNOT ALLOW YOU TO DO SO. IT WOULD ANNOY DURYODHANA. YOU MAY CHOOSE ANYONE OTHER THAN KRISHNA AT YOUR SWAYAMVARA.

"BUT KRISHNA, WHO HAD LEARNT OF HER LOVE ARRIVED AT THE SWAYAMVARA.

LOOK, KRISHNA IS TAKING AWAY MITRAVINDA!

"KING NAGNAJIT OF AYODHYA HAD A DAUGHTER NAMED SATYA. HE MADE AN ANNOUNCEMENT.

I WILL MARRY MY DAUGHTER SATYA TO THE BRAVEST OF MEN

HE MUST BE ABLE TO OVERPOWER THESE SEVEN FEROCIOUS BULLS

"WHEN KRISHNA HEARD OF THIS, HE WENT TO AYODHYA.

LORD KRISHNA IS HERE!

WILL MY DREAMS COME TRUE! WILL HE MARRY ME?

WE ARE INDEED FORTUNATE. I MUST PERSONALLY WELCOME HIM.

O LORD OF THE UNIVERSE! WHAT CAN A MERE MORTAL LIKE ME DO FOR YOU?

I WANT TO BUILD A BOND OF AFFECTION WITH YOU BY MARRYING YOUR DAUGHTER SATYA.

CERTAINLY. WHERE COULD I FIND A BETTER MATCH THAN YOU? BUT I HAVE A CONDITION.

WHAT IS IT?

"NAGNAJIT LED KRISHNA TO THE ENCLOSURE OF THE SEVEN WILD BULLS.

YOU MUST CONTROL THEM AND DISPLAY YOUR PROWESS.

I WILL DO IT.

"KRISHNA ASSUMED SEVEN DIFFERENT FORMS...

WILL HE SUCCEED?

SO MANY KINGS HAVE FAILED TO CONTROL THESE BULLS.

"...AND WITH EASE, HE OVERPOWERED THE FEROCIOUS ANIMALS.

HE HAS DONE IT!

HE IS THE CHOSEN GROOM!

SEE, WITH WHAT EASE HE'S LEADING THE BULLS.

LIKE A CHILD PULLING A TOY!

" THE WEDDING OF KRISHNA WITH SATYA WAS CELEBRATED WITH GREAT JOY AT AYODHYA.

" ACCOMPANIED BY AN ENORMOUS ARMY OF ELEPHANTS, HORSES AND SOLDIERS PRESENTED BY KING NAGNAJIT, THE NEWLY-WEDS LEFT THE TOWN.

" THE KINGS WHO HAD TRIED FOR SATYA'S HAND AND FAILED NOW SURROUNDED THEM.

YOU SHALL NOT GET AWAY WITH HER!

" JUST THEN —

OH, ARJUNA! THERE YOU ARE!

" LIKE A TRUE FRIEND, ARJUNA CAME TO KRISHNA'S AID AND WITH HIS BOW, GANDEEVA, DEFEATED KRISHNA'S OPPONENTS.

THERE! THEY HAVE ALL GONE. YOU CAN PROCEED IN PEACE TO DWARAKA.

LATER KRISHNA MARRIED BHADRA, THE DAUGHTER OF HIS AUNT SHRUTAKEERTI, AND LAKSHMANA, THE PRINCESS OF MADRA.

SO HE HAD EIGHT WIVES?

NO, BESIDES HE MARRIED THE THOUSANDS OF BEAUTIFUL WOMEN HE HAD RESCUED FROM THE CLUTCHES OF THE DEMON NARAKASURA.

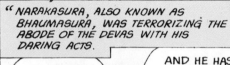

"NARAKASURA, ALSO KNOWN AS BHAUMASURA, WAS TERRORIZING THE ABODE OF THE DEVAS WITH HIS DARING ACTS.

HE HAS EVEN STOLEN THE EAR-RINGS OF MOTHER ADITI. *

AND HE HAS TAKEN AWAY THE UMBRELLA OF VARUNA.

"WITH HIS DEAR WIFE SATYABHAMA, KRISHNA SET OFF ON HIS VEHICLE, THE GARUDA.

"WHEN HE REACHED PRAGJYOTISHAPURA, THE CAPITAL OF NARAKASURA—

HMM! THE MOUNTAINS SURROUND THE CITY LIKE A FORTRESS. AND THEN THERE IS A WALL OF WEAPONS, A MOAT FILLED WITH WATER AND A WELL OF FIRE.

"BESIDES, THE ASURA MURA HAD SPREAD DREADFUL DRAGNETS ALL AROUND. KRISHNA HELD ALOFT HIS MACE...

"...AND WITH IT, HE BROKE THE MOUNTAINS TO PIECES.

* MOTHER OF THE DEVAS.

"NEXT HE TOOK UP HIS BOW.

"AT LAST, HE HURLED HIS CHAKRA*...

"... WHICH DESTROYED THE BARRIERS OF FIRE AND WATER AND TORE UP THE DRAGNETS CREATED BY MURA.

"THE DEMON MURA WHO SLEPT UNDER THE WATER WOKE UP WITH A START.

WHAT'S THAT SOUND? LIKE THE ROAR OF THUNDER!

"IT WAS KRISHNA BLOWING ON THE PANCHAJANYA.

* DISC

"MURA TOOK UP HIS TRIDENT AND RUSHED AT KRISHNA.

AHHH

"HE THREW THE TRIDENT AT GARUDA.

"KRISHNA CUT THE TRIDENT TO PIECES WITH THE ARROWS SHOT IN SUCCESSION...

"...AND AIMED A VOLLEY OF ARROWS AT THE FIVE HEADS OF MURA.

"THE ROAR THAT ROSE FROM HIS FIVE FEROCIOUS HEADS ECHOED FEARFULLY IN ALL DIRECTIONS.

AHHH

"WHATEVER WEAPON THE ASURA CHOSE, KRISHNA DESTROYED WITH EASE. THEN THE ASURA ATTACKED KRISHNA WITH HIS BARE ARMS OUTSTRETCHED.

"PLAYFULLY KRISHNA RELEASED THE SUDARSHANA CHAKRA...

...AND KILLED MURA.

"THE SEVEN SONS OF MURA ARRAYED THEMSELVES TO ATTACK KRISHNA.

COME! LET'S ATTACK HIM WITH ALL OUR WEAPONS! WE MUST AVENGE THE DEATH OF OUR FATHER.

"BUT THEY WERE NO MATCH FOR KRISHNA'S MIGHT. NOW NARAKA-SURA HIMSELF CAME TO THE FORE.

HE HAS KILLED MURA AND HIS SONS HE MUST NOT GO UNPUNISHED.

"WITH HIS ARMY OF HUNDREDS OF ELEPHANTS HE SET FORTH.

WHEN I RELEASE THE SHATAGHNEE* YOU MUST ALL FIRE YOUR ARROWS AT THE SAME TIME.

"WHILE KRISHNA COUNTERED THE ATTACK WITH HIS ARROWS, GARUDA SET UPON THE ENEMY WITH HIS POWERFUL WINGS TO ANNIHILATE THE ELEPHANTS.

* A WEAPON

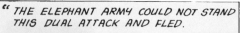

" THE ELEPHANT ARMY COULD NOT STAND THIS DUAL ATTACK AND FLED.

" ONLY NARAKASURA REMAINED ON THE BATTLEFIELD.

THAT BIRD HAS SCARED AWAY MY ELEPHANTS. I WILL KILL HIM WITH MY SHAKTI.*

WHY, HE DID NOT EVEN BUDGE! LET ME ATTACK KRISHNA.

" BUT KRISHNA WAS QUICKER THAN HIM AND...

...THE SUDARSHANA CHAKRA CUT OFF THE ASURA'S HEAD.

" WITH NARAKASURA KILLED, BHOOMI, MOTHER EARTH, APPROACHED KRISHNA.

HERE ARE THE EAR-RINGS OF MOTHER ADITI AND THE UMBRELLA OF VARUNA, STOLEN BY NARAKASURA.

* A WEAPON

"BOWING RESPECTFULLY SHE SAID—

LORD! MY GRANDSON BHAGADATTA, SON OF BHAUMASURA, IS FILLED WITH FEAR. PROTECT HIM.

"KRISHNA BLESSED THE TREMBLING BOY AND THEN ENTERED NARAKASURA'S PALACE.

"HE FOUND SIXTEEN THOUSAND BEAUTIFUL PRINCESSES IMPRISONED INSIDE. THEY HAD BEEN CAPTURED BY THE WICKED NARAKASURA.

LOOK! LORD KRISHNA HIMSELF!

I HOPE HE RESCUES US.

"ALL OF THEM WERE ENRAPTURED BY KRISHNA.

I WANT KRISHNA TO BE MY HUSBAND. MAY GOD GRANT MY ARDENT WISH.

"KRISHNA REALISED THEIR DEVOTION TO HIM AND ARRANGED TO SEND THEM TO DWARAKA.

" LATER KRISHNA AND SATYABHAMA VISITED INDRA'S ABODE AMARAVATI.

HERE ARE THE EAR-RINGS OF MOTHER ADITI.

" SATYABHAMA WAS FASCINATED BY A CELESTIAL TREE — KALPAVRIKSHA.

HOW LOVELY IT LOOKS! CAN'T I HAVE IT?

" KRISHNA FORCED INDRA TO PART WITH THE CELESTIAL TREE AND BROUGHT IT TO DWARAKA.

THERE! YOU CAN HAVE IT GROWING IN THE GARDEN OF YOUR OWN PALACE.

" MEANWHILE, THE THOUSANDS OF DAMSELS RELEASED FROM BHAUMASURA'S PALACE HAD ARRIVED AT DWARAKA.

" EACH OF THEM WAS GIVEN A SEPARATE PALACE TO LIVE IN. THEN, ON AN AUSPICIOUS DAY, KRISHNA ASSUMED MULTIPLE FORMS AND WAS CEREMONIOUSLY WEDDED TO ALL OF THEM AT THE SAME TIME.

"ONE DAY WHEN KRISHNA WAS SITTING IN A RELAXED MOOD WITH RUKMINI—

HOW DEVOTED SHE IS TO ME. BUT LET ME TEASE HER.

DEAR ONE! SO MANY KINGS, RICH AND NOBLE, VIED WITH ONE ANOTHER FOR YOUR HAND IN MARRIAGE. YET YOU REJECTED ALL YOUR SUITORS, AND SELECTED ME, WHO IS NOT YOUR EQUAL IN ANY WAY. WHY?

WHY DID YOU ACCEPT ME? SEE HOW WE YADAVAS HAD TO TAKE REFUGE IN THE SEA TO ESCAPE JARASANDHA. WE HAVE NO RICHES, NO POSSESSIONS.

SURELY YOU KNOW THAT MARRIAGES SHOULD BE AMONG EQUALS — IN WEALTH, SOCIAL STATUS AND AGE. WHY DID YOU PLUNGE HEADLONG INTO THIS ALLIANCE? JUST ON THE BASIS OF SOME FALSE PRAISE YOU HAD HEARD ABOUT ME?

AS FOR MYSELF, I KIDNAPPED YOU JUST TO HUMILIATE RUKMI, YOUR BROTHER.

"ON HEARING THIS, RUKMINI TREMBLED AND FELL INTO A SWOON.

"KRISHNA REALISED HE HAD GONE TOO FAR.

POOR THING. I HAD JUST MEANT TO TEASE HER.

"IN A TRICE HE GOT DOWN AND AFFECTIONATELY LIFTED HER UP.

I WAS JUST TEASING YOU. YOU LOOK SO LOVELY WHEN YOU ARE AGITATED.

ARE YOU SURE YOU SAID ALL THIS IN JEST?

I KNOW I AM NOT EQUAL TO YOU, THE LORD OF ALL WORLDS. BUT MY ONLY DESIRE IS TO STAY BY YOUR SIDE AND SERVE YOU ALL MY LIFE.

I TEASED YOU JUST TO HEAR YOU SAY THIS.

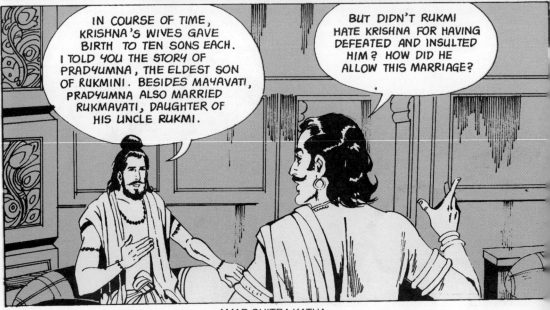

IN COURSE OF TIME, KRISHNA'S WIVES GAVE BIRTH TO TEN SONS EACH. I TOLD YOU THE STORY OF PRADYUMNA, THE ELDEST SON OF RUKMINI. BESIDES MAYAVATI, PRADYUMNA ALSO MARRIED RUKMAVATI, DAUGHTER OF HIS UNCLE RUKMI.

BUT DIDN'T RUKMI HATE KRISHNA FOR HAVING DEFEATED AND INSULTED HIM? HOW DID HE ALLOW THIS MARRIAGE?

"RUKMAVATI, THE LOVELY DAUGHTER OF RUKMI, HAD THE CUSTOMARY SWAYAMVARA.

SURELY! THAT PRINCE IS THE MOST HANDSOME AND CHARMING! I'LL CHOOSE HIM TO BE MY HUSBAND.

"RUKMI SAW THE GARLAND BEING PUT ON PRADYUMNA, SON OF KRISHNA.

SHE HAS CHOSEN PRADYUMNA, SON OF MY ENEMY— THAT KRISHNA.

MY DEAR SISTER RUKMINI WILL BE HAPPY. FOR HER SAKE I WILL LET THEM WED.

"THE KINGS AND PRINCES WHO HAD GATHERED IN THE HALL WERE ENRAGED AND PROTESTED.

"PRADYUMNA FOUGHT THEM BRAVELY, DEFEATED THEM AND CARRIED AWAY RUKMAVATI TO DWARAKA.

"PRADYUMNA AND RUKMAVATI WERE MARRIED WITH DUE CEREMONY. THEY HAD A SON WHO WAS NAMED ANIRUDDHA, WHO GREW UP TO BE AS HANDSOME AS HIS FATHER.

"BANASURA, WHO RULED OVER SHONITAPURA, WAS A GREAT DEVOTEE OF LORD SHIVA. ONE DAY —

AH! LORD SHIVA IS DANCING THE TANDAVA* I WILL USE MY THOUSAND ARMS TO PROVIDE MUSIC.

"BANASURA PLAYED VARIOUS MUSICAL INSTRUMENTS TO ACCOMPANY LORD SHIVA'S DANCE.

I AM PLEASED WITH YOUR DEVOTION. NAME ANY BOON YOU DESIRE.

LORD, REMAIN HERE AND GUARD MY KINGDOM.

"THUS PROTECTED BY LORD SHIVA, BANASURA LIVED IN PEACE. ONE DAY —

LORD! MY ONE THOUSAND HANDS ARE OF NO USE TO ME. THERE IS NO ONE BESIDES YOU WHO CAN MATCH MY STRENGTH. WHOM CAN I FIGHT?

IN FACT, THE OTHER DAY, MY ARMS WERE ITCHING TO FIGHT SO MUCH THAT I CRUSHED A WHOLE RANGE OF MOUNTAINS.

"LORD SHIVA SAID —

YOU FOOL! JUST WAIT! WHEN THE FLAGSTAFF OF YOUR CHARIOT BREAKS OFF, YOU WILL MEET YOUR MATCH AND HE WILL CRUSH YOUR ARROGANCE.

AT LAST! NOW I CAN LOOK FORWARD TO A REAL GOOD FIGHT.

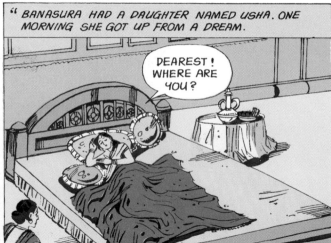

" BANASURA HAD A DAUGHTER NAMED USHA. ONE MORNING SHE GOT UP FROM A DREAM.

DEAREST! WHERE ARE YOU?

" HER COMPANIONS WERE SURPRISED.

WHAT HAPPENED, USHA?

OH! I JUST HAD A STRANGE DREAM.

" CHITRALEKHA, WHO WAS USHA'S CLOSE FRIEND SAID —

BUT WHOM DID YOU DREAM OF?

I DON'T KNOW! I HAD NEVER MET HIM BEFORE.

ALL I CAN TELL YOU IS THAT HE WAS DARK AND HANDSOME WITH LARGE LOTUS-SHAPED EYES.

"CHITRALEKHA, WHO WAS A SKILLED ARTIST SET TO WORK.

NOW, I WILL DRAW THE PORTRAITS OF KINGS AND SAGES. SEE IF YOU CAN RECOGNISE THE MAN OF YOUR DREAM.

IS IT ANY OF THESE?

NO, NO, NO.

"AT LAST —

AH! THERE HE IS. THAT'S MY LORD.

THIS IS ANIRUDDHA, GRANDSON OF KRISHNA. BEFORE LONG, I WILL BRING HIM TO YOU.

"CHITRALEKHA USED THE ART OF YOGA AND BROUGHT ANIRUDDHA TO SHONITAPURA FROM DWARAKA.

"USHA AND ANIRUDDHA SPENT MANY HAPPY DAYS IN HER HEAVILY GUARDED PALACE.

"AFTER A WHILE THE GUARDS NOTICED THAT USHA HAD NOT COME OUT OF THE PALACE FOR DAYS.

COULD SHE BE SICK?

NO! I ALWAYS HEAR THE SOUND OF MUSIC AND LAUGHTER FROM INSIDE.

AND A MAN'S VOICE TOO!

"THEY REPORTED THE MATTER TO BANASURA.

WE HAVE GUARDED HER PALACE DAY AND NIGHT.

YET WE FEEL A MAN HAS GOT INSIDE.

"BANASURA CHARGED INTO USHA'S PALACE.

"HE WAS STUNNED TO SEE ANIRUDDHA CALMLY PLAYING DICE WITH USHA.

CAPTURE HIM! TIE HIM UP WITH SERPENT-BONDS.*

" MEANWHILE, DWARAKA WAS PLUNGED IN GLOOM.

IT HAS BEEN FOUR MONTHS NOW SINCE ANIRUDDHA DISAPPEARED.

AH! THERE IS NARADA. PERHAPS HE WILL HAVE SOME NEWS.

" WHEN NARADA RELATED HOW BANASURA HAD CAPTURED ANIRUDDHA, THE PEOPLE OF DWARAKA WERE FILLED WITH RAGE.

ATTACK BANASURA.

ON TO SHONITAPURA.

" KRISHNA LED THE ATTACK AND ARRANGED HIS TROOP IN A FORMIDABLE FORMATION.

SURROUND HIS CAPITAL!

" BANASURA EMERGED WITH AN EQUALLY LARGE FORCE. WITH HIM WERE LORD SHIVA AND HIS SON KARTTIKEYA.

COME! PRADYUMNA, YOU FIGHT KARTTIKEYA. WHILE I CONFRONT SHIVA. SATYAKI, YOU TAKE ON BANASURA.

AMAR CHITRA KATHA

"LORD SHIVA USED HIS POWERFUL CELESTIAL WEAPONS BUT KRISHNA REPELLED THEM WITH EQUALLY STRONG BUT OPPOSING WEAPONS.

HE IS USING THE AGNEYASTRA, I'LL QUELL IT WITH THE PARJANYASTRA.

I'LL USE THE JRUMBHANASTRA TO MAKE SHIVA SLEEP. THEN I CAN ATTACK THE REST OF THE ARMY.

"THE JRUMBHANASTRA MADE SHIVA SO DROWSY THAT HE COULD NOT FIGHT.

YAWN.

"BANASURA REALISED THAT HIS ARMY WAS BEING DESTROYED AND LUNGED AT KRISHNA.

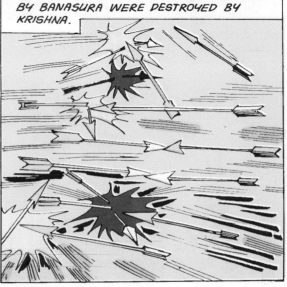

"BUT THE HUNDREDS OF ARROWS RELEASED BY BANASURA WERE DESTROYED BY KRISHNA.

"WHEN BANASURA'S CHARIOT, CHARIOTEER AND HORSES FELL UNDER KRISHNA'S ATTACK HE RAN AWAY FROM THE FIELD.

"BUT SOON HE RETURNED WITH VARIOUS WEAPONS IN HIS MANY HANDS.

"KRISHNA RELEASED HIS SUDARSHANA CHAKRA.

"WHEN BANASURA'S ARMS BEGAN TO FALL OFF LIKE TENDER BRANCHES OF A TREE, SHIVA INTERVENED.

BANASURA IS UNDER MY PROTECTION. SPARE HIM HIS LIFE.

I WILL NOT SLAY HIM. BUT TO HUMBLE HIS PRIDE, I WILL CUT OFF ALL BUT FOUR OF HIS ARMS.

" BANASURA BOWED IN GRATITUDE TO KRISHNA AND ORDERED THE RELEASE OF ANIRUDDHA

" WITH USHA AND ANIRUDDHA, KRISHNA RETURNED VICTORIOUS TO DWARAKA WHERE THEY RECEIVED A JOYOUS WELCOME.

" ONE DAY, WHILE BALARAMA WAS AWAY VISITING BRAJA, KRISHNA RECEIVED A MESSENGER FROM PAUNDRAKA, THE KING OF KARUSHA, WHO WAS A FRIEND OF NARAKASURA.

HE HAS ASKED YOU TO GIVE YOURSELF UP OR FIGHT.

MY KING HAS SENT A MESSAGE THAT HE IS THE TRUE VAASUDEVA. YOU ARE AN IMPOSTOR WHO CARRIES HIS INSIGNIA.

HA! HA!

WHAT A SILLY MAN.

TELL YOUR KING THAT I WILL NOT GIVE UP MY DISC AND OTHER INSIGNIA. IN FACT, I WILL USE MY DISC TO DESTROY HIM AND HIS FOOLISH FRIENDS WHO MISLEAD HIM INTO THIS SELF-DECEPTION.

" AFTER THE MESSENGER LEFT—

COME! LET US PREPARE TO ATTACK THAT FOOL PAUNDRAKA.

BUT HE IS STAYING WITH HIS FRIEND, THE KING OF KASHI.

" KRISHNA LED HIS ARMY TO KASHI... PAUNDRAKA AND THE KING OF KASHI CAME OUT TO MEET HIS CHALLENGE.

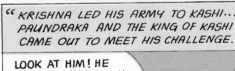

LOOK AT HIM! HE IS DRESSED EXACTLY LIKE ME - WITH A CONCH SHELL, A DISC, A MACE, A DAGGER AND EVEN THE YELLOW GARMENTS! HA! HA! HA!

" ROARING WITH LAUGHTER AT THE SIGHT OF THE IMPOSTOR PAUNDRAKA, KRISHNA ATTACKED THE COMBINED ARMIES OF KASHI AND KARUSHA.

"THEN —

HEY! YOU PAUNDRAKA! YOU WANTED MY CHAKRA AND OTHER WEAPONS, DIDN'T YOU?

WELL, HERE YOU ARE!

IN A MATTER OF MOMENTS, PAUNDRAKA'S HEAD LAY ON THE GROUND.

" NOW KRISHNA TURNED TO THE KING OF KASHI. WITH HIS SUDARSHANA CHAKRA KRISHNA CUT OFF HIS HEAD ALSO.

" OFF FLEW THE HEAD OF THE KING OF KASHI. AND LANDED AT THE GATES OF HIS PALACE.

" SUDAKSHINA, THE PRINCE OF KASHI, WAS SHOCKED AT THE SIGHT.

WHY! THIS IS THE HEAD OF MY FATHER. I MUST AVENGE HIS DEATH.

197

"HE CONCENTRATED HIS ENERGIES TO FIND A METHOD OF REVENGE. ONE DAY, WHILE PERFORMING A YAJNA —

"THE FIRE FIEND THAT EMERGED RUSHED TO DWARAKA.

"THE PEOPLE OF DWARAKA WERE TERRIFIED.

LORD! SAVE US FROM THIS CALAMITY.

"KRISHNA BARELY LOOKED UP FROM HIS GAME OF DICE.

DON'T WORRY. I WILL PROTECT YOU.

" HE ORDERED HIS SUDARSHANA CHAKRA TO ATTACK THE FIEND.

" WHIRRING MENACINGLY, THE DISC SET OUT TO DESTROY THE FIEND.

THE DISK FOLLOWED THE FIRE FIEND TO KASHI. AFTER DESTROYING THE FIEND, THE SUDARSHANA CHAKRA WAS RESTORED TO LORD KRISHNA.

THUS ENDS THE SEVENTH SESSION OF OUR RENDERING OF THE TENTH CHAPTER OF THE BHAGAWAT PURANA.

KRISHNA: AN ALLY OF THE PANDAVAS

PAREEKSHIT WHO HAD BEEN LISTENING WITH RAPT ATTENTION TO SHUKADEVA NOW INTERRUPTED THE SAGE'S NARRATION OF KRISHNA'S EXPLOITS.

DO TELL ME THE ADVENTURES OF THE GALLANT BALARAMA.

ONCE WHILE BALARAMA WAS JOURNEYING ON MOUNT RAIVATAKA, HE MET AN APE CALLED **DVIVIDA**.

"DVIVIDA, WHO WAS SAID TO POSSESS THE STRENGTH OF TEN THOUSAND ELEPHANTS, WAS ENRAGED BY THE SLAYING OF NARAKA-SURA.

I MUST AVENGE THE DEATH OF MY DEAR FRIEND NARAKASURA.

" HE CREATED HAVOC IN THE REGION OF ANARTA.*

THIS IS WHERE THAT KRISHNA, THE SLAYER OF MY FRIEND, LIVES. I WILL RAVAGE THIS WHOLE AREA.

" HE THREW HUGE BOULDERS ON HOUSES.

"HE STOOD IN THE SEA AND CHURNED THE WATER WITH HIS HANDS...

"...TILL THE COASTAL VILLAGES WERE SUBMERGED.

✱ CORRESPONDING TO MODERN SAURASHTRA

"HE KIDNAPPED PEOPLE AND HELD THEM CAPTIVE.

THERE! NOW THEY WILL NEVER BE ABLE TO ESCAPE.

"ONE DAY AS HE WAS BUSY HARASSING THE INHABITANTS, THE SOUND OF MUSIC DREW HIM TO RAIVATAKA HILL.

I WONDER WHERE THE MUSIC IS COMING FROM.

"IT WAS HERE THAT HE SAW BALARAMA.

"DVIVIDA GRINNED AND CHATTERED IN ANGER. TO FRIGHTEN THE WOMEN HE VIOLENTLY SHOOK THE BRANCHES OF THE TREES. THIS DREW LAUGHTER FROM THEM.

HEE! HEE!

I WILL TEACH THEM A LESSON FOR LAUGHING AT ME.

"AS HE ADVANCED MENACINGLY TOWARDS THE LADIES —

HEY! GO AWAY!

"DVIVIDA NOW PICKED UP A JAR AND BROKE IT.

HOW DARE YOU! JUST WAIT!

"WHEN DVIVIDA SAW BALARAMA APPROACHING HIM WITH HIS FAVOURITE WEAPONS, HE UPROOTED A SALA TREE.

"BUT BALARAMA PARRIED THE BLOW WITH HIS LEFT HAND AND HIT DVIVIDA WITH HIS PESTLE.

"DVIVIDA'S HEAD WAS CRACKED OPEN BUT HE FOUGHT ON USING TREES AND ROCKS AS WEAPONS.

"BUT THEY WERE ALL CRUSHED BY BALARAMA. FINALLY DVIVIDA LUNGED AT HIM, BAREHANDED.

"BALARAMA CLENCHED HIS FIST AND HIT AT THE COLLAR BONE OF DVIVIDA. THE APE COLLAPSED AND THE ENTIRE FOREST SHOOK AS HE FELL.

"WHEN BALARAMA RETURNED TO DWARAKA, HE WAS WARMLY RECEIVED BY THE CITIZENS.

GOOD THAT YOU KILLED THAT DVIVIDA.

HE HAD BEEN TERRORISING THE PEOPLE.

"IT WAS SOME TIME AFTER THIS EVENT THAT PRINCE DURYODHANA ARRANGED THE SWAYAMVARA OF HIS DAUGHTER, LAKSHMANA. IT WAS ATTENDED BY KINGS AND PRINCES FROM FAR AND NEAR.

LOOK! THAT YOUNG MAN IS TAKING THE BRIDE AWAY.

WHO IS HE?

HE IS SAMBA, THE SON OF KRISHNA AND JAMBAVATI.

KARNA, SEIZE HIM.

"KARNA, DURYODHANA AND OTHERS FOLLOWED SAMBA.

WE WILL CAPTURE HIM. LET THE YADAVAS COME AND FREE HIM THEN.

"BUT KRISHNA'S SON FACED THE WARRIORS ALONE.

"HE SHOT ARROW AFTER ARROW TO COUNTER THEIR ATTACK.

LET US SURROUND HIM. YOU ATTACK HIS HORSE WHILE I AIM AT THE CHARIOTEER.

"AT LAST THE KAURAVA WARRIORS OVERPOWERED SAMBA.

"SAMBA WAS TIED UP AND TAKEN CAPTIVE TO HASTINAPURA.

"IT WAS NARADA, AS USUAL WHO CONVEYED THIS NEWS TO THE YADAVAS.

THE KAURAVAS HAVE CAPTURED SAMBA.

HOW DARE THEY DO SO? WE WILL ATTACK THEM WITH OUR ARMY.

"BALARAMA INTERVENED —

LET US AVOID ANY FIGHTS IN THE FAMILY. I MYSELF WILL GO TO HASTINA-PURA AND PERSUADE THEM TO FREE SAMBA.

"ACCOMPANIED BY SOME WISE OLD MEN, BALARAMA SET OUT FOR HASTINAPURA.

WE WILL STOP HERE OUTSIDE THE CITY UDDHAVA, YOU GO TO KING DHRITARASHTRA AND FIND OUT WHAT THEIR INTENTIONS ARE.

"UDDHAVA ARRIVED AT THE KAURAVA COURT.

SHRI BALARAMA IS HERE TO SEE YOU.

HE IS MOST WELCOME.

"BALARAMA WAS WARMLY WELCOMED BY THE KAURAVAS AFTER GREETING THEM BALARAMA SAID—

I HAVE A MESSAGE FOR YOU FROM OUR KING UGRASENA LISTEN PATIENTLY.

WE KNOW THAT YOUR WARRIORS SURROUNDED AND OVERPOWERED SAMBA IN AN UNJUST MANNER.

WE WANT TO AVOID ANY FAMILY FEUDS HENCE WE DO NOT PROTEST OR FIGHT.

BUT NOW IT WOULD BE BEST IF YOU RELEASE SAMBA AND RETURN HIM TO US WITH HIS NEWLY-WED WIFE.

"BALARAMA'S GENTLE REQUEST WAS NOT WELL RECEIVED BY THE KAURAVAS.

HA! YOU YADAVAS REALLY THINK TOO MUCH OF YOURSELF.

JUST BECAUSE YOU ARE RELATED TO US BY MARRIAGE, IT DOES NOT MAKE YOU OUR EQUAL IN STATUS.

SO FAR WE DID NOT OBJECT TO YOUR USE OF THE ROYAL INSIGNIA BUT SINCE YOU ARE TRYING TO DICTATE TERMS TO US, WE WILL HAVE TO PUT YOU IN YOUR PLACE.

"ARROGANTLY THE KAURAVAS WALKED AWAY WITHOUT EVEN WAITING FOR BALARAMA'S REPLY.

" BALARAMA WAS ENRAGED BY THIS INSULT.

I STOPPED OUR PEOPLE FROM WAGING A WAR WITH OUR KINSMEN, THE KAURAVAS BUT I WAS WRONG.

THESE KAURAVAS ARE ASKING FOR A FIGHT WELL, THERE'S ONLY ONE WAY OF PUTTING THEM IN THEIR PLACE.

" BALARAMA HELD ALOFT HIS PLOUGH MENACINGLY.

TODAY I WILL RENDER THE EARTH FREE FROM THESE VAIN AND FOOLISH KAURAVAS.

" NO SOONER THAN BALARAMA'S WEAPON TOUCHED THE GROUND—

THE EARTH IS SHAKING!

"THE KAURAVAS WERE PANIC-STRICKEN.

STOP HIM!

HELP!

HE WILL DROWN OUR CITY IN THE GANGA.

"THEY HURRIEDLY RELEASED SAMBA.

HERE IS YOUR SAMBA AND LAKSHMANA, HIS WIFE.

"WITH FOLDED HANDS THEY APPROACHED BALARAMA.

FORGIVE US. IT WAS FOOLISH OF US TO INSULT YOU. SPARE OUR CITY AND OUR PEOPLE.

"ALL THE CITIZENS OF HASTINAPURA BESEECHED BALARAMA.

SAVE US!

HAVE MERCY!

"BALARAMA'S ANGER WAS EASILY AROUSED BUT ALSO EASILY PACIFIED.

DO NOT BE AFRAID. I WILL SPARE YOU.

"DURYODHANA, WHO LOVED HIS DAUGHTER LAKSHMANA DEARLY, GAVE HER GENEROUS PRESENTS.

"FOLLOWED BY A RETINUE OF ELEPHANTS, HORSES AND CHARIOTS GIFTED TO THE BRIDE, BALARAMA RETURNED TO DWARAKA WITH THE NEWLY-WEDS.

"BALARAMA RELATED THE EVENTS IN THE COURT OF DWARAKA.

THIS IS HOW OUR SAMBA WON THE HAND OF LAKSHMANA.

SHUKADEVA PAUSED FOR EFFECT.

TILL TODAY, THE CITY OF HASTINAPURA IS RAISED AT THE SOUTHERN END AND INCLINED TOWARDS THE GANGA, EVIDENCE OF BALARAMA'S PROWESS.

"ONE DAY, NARADA DECIDED TO VISIT KRISHNA.

KRISHNA HAS MARRIED THOUSANDS OF PRINCESSES, THOSE WHOM HE RESCUED FROM THE CLUTCHES OF NARAKASURA. I MUST SEE HOW HE SPENDS HIS DAY AT DWARAKA.

"WHEN NARADA ARRIVED AT THE RESPLENDENT CITY OF DWARAKA, HE BEHELD THE BEAUTIFUL INNER CHAMBERS OF THE QUEENS.

AH! PILLARS MADE OF CORAL, BALCONIES OF LAPIS-LAZULI AND SAPPHIRE WALLS. VISHWA-KARMA HAS REALLY DIS-PLAYED HIS ART IN THIS PALACE.

"NARADA FOUND KRISHNA IN RUKMINI'S PALACE.

WELCOME, O NARADA!

"AFTER EXCHANGING PLEASANTRIES WITH KRISHNA AND RUKMINI, NARADA'S CURIOSITY LED HIM TO THE PALACES OF THE OTHER QUEENS.

"HE WAS ASTONISHED AT THE SIGHT THAT MET HIS EYES IN THE VARIOUS PALACES.

"HE SAW KRISHNA PLAYING CHESS IN ONE.

"WHILE IN ANOTHER KRISHNA APPEARED TO BE ENGROSSED IN PERFORMING A YAJNA.

"HE BEHELD KRISHNA ROMPING PLAYFULLY WITH HIS CHILDREN IN ONE ROOM.

"WHILE A MINUTE LATER, HE SAW KRISHNA IN SERIOUS DISCUSSION WITH LEARNED PANDITS.

"BEFORE LEAVING, NARADA TURNED TO KRISHNA, AND SAID —

O LORD, YOU ALONE AMONG THE GODS ARE CAPABLE OF INDULGING IN SUCH HUMAN ACTIVITIES.

"ONE DAY WHILE KRISHNA WAS IN THE COUNCIL HALL CALLED SUDHARMA SABHA, A STRANGER RUSHED IN —

O LORD, YOU ARE THE SAVIOUR OF ALL. I HAVE COME TO SEEK YOUR HELP.

"HE WAS THE MESSENGER SENT ON BEHALF OF THE THOUSANDS OF KINGS HELD CAPTIVE BY JARASANDHA IN GIRIVRAJA.

THE IMPRISONED KINGS HAVE IMPLORED YOU TO HELP THEM.

JARASANDHA WAS DEFEATED SEVENTEEN TIMES BY YOU. IT WAS ONLY TO DISPLAY YOUR HUMAN FRAILTY THAT YOU ALLOWED HIM TO DEFEAT YOU ON THE EIGHTEENTH OCCASION.

BUT THIS ONE VICTORY HAS MADE JARASANDHA MORE ARROGANT THAN HE EVER WAS.

THE CAPTURED KINGS DEPEND ON YOUR HELP, O KRISHNA.

"JUST THEN NARADA ARRIVED ON THE SCENE. AFTER WELCOMING HIM WITH DUE RESPECT, KRISHNA SAID —

O NARADA, YOU ROAM FREELY IN THE THREE WORLDS. TELL US, HOW ARE YUDHISHTHIRA AND THE OTHER PANDAVAS?

LORD, YOU JUST PRETEND TO BE IGNORANT OF WHAT GOES ON. NOTHING ESCAPES YOUR ATTENTION.

I WILL ANSWER YOUR QUESTION ALL THE SAME THE PANDAVAS ARE WELL AND HAPPY. HOWEVER, THEY WOULD LIKE YOU TO BE PRESENT AT THE RAJASOOYA YAJNA THEY PLAN TO PERFORM.

"KRISHNA SEEMED UNCERTAIN ABOUT HIS NEXT MOVE.

WE SHOULD ATTACK JARASANDHA FIRST.

YES, IT IS MORE IMPORTANT TO RELEASE THOSE KINGS.

"KRISHNA TURNED TO UDDHAVA—

UDDHAVA, I HAVE FAITH IN YOUR WISE COUNSEL WHAT DO YOU THINK WE SHOULD DO IN THE PRESENT CIRCUMSTANCES?

SAGE NARADA HAS ASKED YOU TO ATTEND THE RAJASOOYA YAJNA OF YOUR COUSINS, THE PANDAVAS IT IS FITTING FOR YOU TO BE THERE BUT OF EQUAL IMPORT- ANCE IS THE TASK OF HELPING THE KINGS WHO HAVE SOUGHT YOUR PROTECTION.

TO PERFORM A RAJASOOYA YAJNA, THE PANDAVAS WILL HAVE TO GAIN SUPREMACY OVER THE ENTIRE LAND.

JARASANDHA WILL HAVE TO BE DEFEATED IN EITHER CASE SO THAT THE RAJASOOYA YAJNA CAN BE PERFORMED OR TO HELP THE KINGS HELD PRISONERS BY HIM.

BHEEMA CAN EASILY OVERPOWER JARASANDHA IN A DUEL. SINCE JARASANDHA IS KNOWN TO BE GENEROUS TO BRAHMINS, BHEEMA COULD GO DISGUISED AS A BRAHMIN.

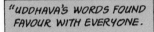

"UDDHAVA'S WORDS FOUND FAVOUR WITH EVERYONE.

A GOOD IDEA.

YES, I AGREE.

"SOON KRISHNA, ACCOMPANIED BY HIS WIVES AND CHILDREN, SET OUT FOR INDRAPRASTHA.

"BEFORE LEAVING DWARAKA, HE ASSURED THE MESSENGER FROM GIRIVRAJA.

GO AND TELL THE KINGS NOT TO BE AFRAID. I WILL SOON COME AND SLAY JARASANDHA.

"AFTER SEVERAL DAYS OF TRAVEL, TRAVERSING MOUNTAINS AND RIVERS, KRISHNA AND HIS ARMY REACHED INDRAPRASTHA.

"THE PANDAVAS WERE OVERJOYED TO SEE THEIR BELOVED KRISHNA.

"KUNTI RUSHED TO GREET HER DEAR NEPHEW.

"DRAUPADI WELCOMED KRISHNA'S WIVES RUKMINI, SATYABHAMA, JAMBAVATI, KALINDI, MITRAVINDA, BHADRA, SATYA AND LAKSHMANA WITH PRESENTS OF GARMENTS, JEWELS AND FLOWERS.

"KRISHNA AND HIS ARMY WERE PROVIDED WITH COMFORTABLE PALACES IN INDRA-PRASTHA AND SPENT MANY HAPPY DAYS THERE.

"ONE DAY AT COURT, YUDHISHTHIRA SAID—

O KRISHNA, I WISH TO PERFORM THE RAJASOOYA YAJNA I REQUEST YOU TO HELP ME IN THIS TASK.

IT IS AN EXCELLENT IDEA. THE RAJASOOYA YAJNA WILL HELP TO SPREAD YOUR FAME IN THE LAND. FIRST YOU MUST SUBDUE ALL THE KINGS OF THE LAND AND COLLECT THE REQUISITE MATERIAL.

NO KING ON EARTH WILL DARE TO REFUSE THE SUPREMACY OF A PERSON LIKE YOU.

"YUDHISHTHIRA WAS DELIGHTED TO HEAR THIS. ENTHUSED BY KRISHNA'S ENCOURAGEMENT HE GAVE INSTRUCTIONS TO HIS BROTHERS.

SAHADEVA, YOU GO TO THE COUNTRIES IN THE SOUTH. NAKULA WILL PROCEED TO THE WEST WITH THE WARRIORS OF MATSYA*

ARJUNA AND THE ARMY OF KEKAYA WILL PROCEED TO THE NORTH WHILE THE BRAVE WARRIORS OF MADRA WILL BE LED TO THE EAST BY BHEEMA.

"AS INSTRUCTED BY YUDHISHTHIRA, THE FOUR BROTHERS SET OUT TO CONQUER THE VARIOUS REGIONS.

* KINGDOM RULED BY VIRATA

" THEY RETURNED VICTORIOUS, LADEN WITH THE TREASURES GIFTED BY THE CONQUERED KINGS.

HERE IT IS, THE WEALTH FROM THE KINGS WHO HAVE SURRENDERED TO YOUR SUPREMACY.

HAVE ALL THE KINGS AGREED?

YES, EXCEPT JARASANDHA.

" SEEING YUDHISHTHIRA'S ENTHUSIASM BEING DAMPENED BY THIS NEWS, KRISHNA SAID —

UDDHAVA HAD SUGGEST-ED A WAY OF CONQUERING JARASANDHA.

" HE THEN UNFOLDED HIS PLAN.

" SOON BHEEMA, ARJUNA AND KRISHNA REACHED GIRIVRAJA, THE CAPITAL OF JARASANDHA, IN THE GUISE OF BRAHMINS.

"WHEN THEY ARRIVED AT JARASANDHA'S PALACE —

GLORY TO YOU, O KING WE HAVE TRAVELLED FROM AFAR WITH A SPECIFIC PURPOSE. DO GRANT US OUR REQUEST.

DO NOT DISAPPOINT US, O KING.

YOU KNOW HOW HARISHCHANDRA, RANTIDEVA, SHIBI AND BALI, ATTAINED SALVATION BY GIVING AWAY ALL THEY HAD TO THEIR GUESTS.

"JARASANDHA WAS NOT FOOLED BY THEIR DISGUISE.

THEY APPEAR TO BE KSHATRIYAS, NOT BRAHMINS. THE MARKS OF THE BOW ARE SO CLEAR ON THEIR WRISTS.

YET, PROBABLY IT IS OUT OF FEAR OF ME THAT THEY ARE IN DISGUISE. I WILL GIVE THEM WHATEVER THEY ASK.

"ALOUD HE SAID —

O BRAHMINS, TELL ME WHAT YOU DESIRE. I AM EVEN READY TO GIVE UP MY LIFE FOR YOU.

"KRISHNA SAID —

WE ARE NOT BRAHMINS IN SEARCH OF ALMS WE ARE KSHATRIYAS KEEN ON FIGHTING WE WANT A DUEL WITH YOU THAT IS THE ALMS WE SEEK.

THIS IS PANDU'S SON BHEEMA AND THIS IS HIS BROTHER ARJUNA I AM THEIR COUSIN AND YOUR ARCH ENEMY KRISHNA.

"JARASANDHA ROARED WITH LAUGHTER.

YOU FOOLS! IF IT IS A FIGHT YOU WANT, I WILL HAPPILY GRANT YOUR WISH.

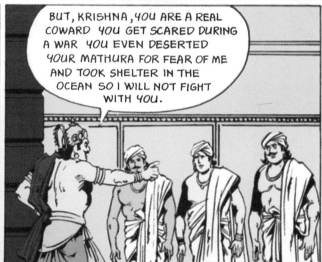

BUT, KRISHNA, YOU ARE A REAL COWARD YOU GET SCARED DURING A WAR YOU EVEN DESERTED YOUR MATHURA FOR FEAR OF ME AND TOOK SHELTER IN THE OCEAN SO I WILL NOT FIGHT WITH YOU.

ARJUNA IS NOT STRONG ENOUGH TO BE MY EQUAL, SO I SHALL NOT FIGHT WITH HIM.

THAT LEAVES ONLY YOU, BHEEMA HERE, TAKE THIS MACE.

"TAKING UP ANOTHER MACE HIMSELF JARASANDHA LED BHEEMA TO THE OUTSKIRTS OF THE CITY.

"LIKE TWO MIGHTY ELEPHANTS FIGHTING, BHEEMA AND JARASANDHA WERE PITCHED AGAINST ONE ANOTHER.

"SUCH WAS THE IMPACT OF THEIR BLOWS THAT BOTH THEIR MACES WERE SOON CRUSHED TO PIECES.

"BAREHANDED, THEY BEGAN TO WRESTLE WITH ONE ANOTHER.

"BEING WELL MATCHED IN STRENGTH, SPIRIT AND SKILL, THE FIGHT WENT ON AND ON FOR DAYS.

"THEY WOULD STOP THE FIGHT AT DUSK AND RESUME AT DAWN.

WAKE UP, BHEEMA, IT IS TIME TO START AGAIN.

"AT THE END OF THE TWENTY-SEVENTH DAY BHEEMA CONFIDED TO KRISHNA.

O KRISHNA, I CANNOT DEFEAT JARASANDHA.

"ON THE TWENTY-EIGHTH DAY, AS THE FIGHT WAS GOING ON —

IT WAS THE DEMONESS JARA WHO GAVE LIFE TO JARASANDHA AS AN INFANT BY PUTTING TWO HALVES OF HIS BODY TOGETHER.

"TO GIVE A HINT TO BHEEMA KRISHNA TOOK UP A TWIG IN HIS HAND AND BROKE IT INTO TWO.

"AT THE FIRST OPPORTUNITY, BHEEMA FELLED JARASANDHA TO THE GROUND.

"WITH A SINGLE STROKE, BHEEMA TORE JARASANDHA'S BODY INTO TWO.

"AMIDST THE LOUD CRIES OF THE SPECTATORS, ARJUNA AND KRISHNA EMBRACED BHEEMA.

"JARASANDHA'S SON SAHADEVA WAS INSTALLED AS THE KING BY KRISHNA.

LET US NOW FREE THE KINGS.

"THE THOUSANDS OF KINGS WHO HAD BEEN IMPRISONED BY JARASANDHA IN A FORT WERE FREED AT LAST.

"THEIR WEARY AND WORN FACES LIT UP WHEN THEY BEHELD KRISHNA IN HIS DIVINE FORM.

YOU ARE INDEED THE REMOVER OF ALL TROUBLES AND FEARS, O KRISHNA.

"KRISHNA SAID— IT WAS THE VANITY OF THEIR POSSESSIONS THAT LED THE LIKES OF RAVANA, HEHAYA AND NAHUSHA TO LOSE THEIR POSITIONS WITH YOUR SENSES UNDER CONTROL AND YOUR MIND FIRM, LOOK AFTER THE SUBJECTS OF YOUR KINGDOM.

"THEREAFTER KRISHNA ARRANGED FOR THE KINGS TO BE BATHED AND REFRESHED UNDER KRISHNA'S GUIDANCE, THE NEW KING SAHADEVA GAVE THEM PRESENTS BEFITTING ROYAL GUESTS.

"THE VARIOUS KINGS WENT BACK TO THEIR KINGDOMS ON BEJEWELLED CHARIOTS, SINGING THE PRAISES OF KRISHNA ON THEIR WAY.

"LATER, KRISHNA, ARJUNA AND BHEEMA TOO RETURNED TO INDRAPRASTHA. THE SOUND OF THEIR CONCH-SHELLS ANNOUNCED THEIR ARRIVAL."

KRISHNA AND ARJUNA ARE BACK.

JARASANDHA MUST HAVE BEEN DEFEATED.

O KING! NOW YOU CAN BEGIN YOUR RAJASOOYA YAJNA.

YUDHISHTHIRA'S EYES DIMMED WITH TEARS OF JOY WHEN HE MET KRISHNA.

O KRISHNA, YOU ARE THE LORD OF ALL WORLDS, YET LIKE AN ACTOR YOU INDULGE IN THESE HUMAN ACTIVITIES.

"WITH KRISHNA'S PERMISSION, YUDHISHTHIRA BEGAN THE PREPARATIONS FOR THE YAJNA."

INVITE WELL-VERSED BRAHMINS LIKE VYASA, BHARADWAJA, GAUTAMA, KANVA AND DHAUMYA TO PARTICIPATE IN THE YAJNA.

FORMAL INVITATIONS MUST BE SENT TO DRONACHARYA, BHEESHMA, KRIPACHARYA, TO KING DHRITARASHTRA AND DURYODHANA AS WELL AS TO THE WISE VIDURA.

"AN OPEN INVITATION WAS ANNOUNCED FOR PEOPLE FROM ALL WALKS OF LIFE TO ATTEND THE YAJNA."

"AS PER CUSTOM, THE LAND CONSECRATED FOR THE YAJNA WAS PLOUGHED WITH A GOLDEN PLOUGH BY YUDHISHTHIRA.

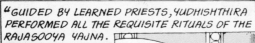

"GUIDED BY LEARNED PRIESTS, YUDHISHTHIRA PERFORMED ALL THE REQUISITE RITUALS OF THE RAJASOOYA YAJNA.

NOW THE MAIN CERE-MONIES ARE OVER TO WHOM WILL YOU OFFER THE FIRST WORSHIP?

"EVERYONE PRESENT HAD A DIFFERENT OPINION AS TO WHO MERITED THE HONOUR OF BEING OFFERED THE FIRST WORSHIP SAHADEVA SAID —

SHRI KRISHNA IS THE BEST AMONG THE ASSEMBLED PEOPLE HERE AND HE ALONE DESERVES THE HONOUR WORSHIPPING HIM IS LIKE WORSHIPPING THE ENTIRE CREATION.

" SAHADEVA'S PROPOSAL WAS HEARTILY WELCOMED.

VERY CORRECT.

SAHADEVA IS RIGHT.

WELL SAID.

" YUDHISHTHIRA WAS DELIGHTED TO HEAR THIS AND JOYFULLY BEGAN TO OFFER PRAYERS TO KRISHNA.

"WHEN HE GIFTED YELLOW SILK GARMENTS AND COSTLY JEWELS TO KRISHNA THE HALL WAS FILLED WITH JOYOUS CHEERS OF FELICITATION.

HAIL KRISHNA!

"SHISHUPALA, THE PRINCE OF CHEDI, COULD NOT BEAR ALL THIS.

HOW CAN YOU PEOPLE BE MISLED BY A YOUNG FOOL LIKE SAHADEVA? WITH SO MANY LEARNED VENERABLE SAGES PRESENT HERE, HOW CAN YOU SELECT A COW-HERD LIKE KRISHNA FOR THE FIRST WOR-SHIP?

HE BELONGS TO NO CASTE OR CREED NOR DOES HE HAVE ANY VIRTUES HE IS A BLOT ON HIS FAMILY'S HONOUR.

"KRISHNA CALMLY HEARD SHISHUPALA'S BITTER OUTBURSTS.

"BUT THE OTHERS COULD NOT BEAR TO HEAR KRISHNA BEING INSULTED WHILE SOME PEOPLE LEFT THE PLACE IN DISGUST, OTHERS TOOK UP ARMS TO ATTACK SHISHUPALA.

"WHEN SHISHUPALA CHALLENGED HIS OPPONENTS, KRISHNA STOOD UP AND TRIED TO CALM THEM DOWN.

"BUT WHEN SHISHUPALA LUNGED AT HIM, KRISHNA RELEASED HIS CHAKRA AND CUT OFF HIS HEAD.

"AFTER COMPLETION OF THE YAJNA, YUDHISHTHIRA PROCEEDED FOR HIS RITUAL BATH IN THE GANGA. HE WAS ACCOMPANIED BY HORDES OF PEOPLE, SINGING, DANCING AND MERRY MAKING.

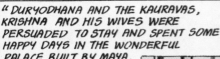

"DURYODHANA AND THE KAURAVAS, KRISHNA AND HIS WIVES WERE PERSUADED TO STAY AND SPENT SOME HAPPY DAYS IN THE WONDERFUL PALACE BUILT BY MAYA.

"THE SUCCESSFUL COMPLETION OF THE RAJASOOYA YAJNA WAS A SOURCE OF JOY FOR EVERYONE EXCEPT DURYO- DHANA. HE BURNED WITH ENVY SEEING THE INCREASED WEALTH AND GLORY OF THE PANDAVAS.

EVERYONE TALKS ONLY OF YUDHISHTHIRA'S GLORY AND HIS YAJNA.

" ONE DAY HE WAS CONFUSED AS HE AMBLED ALONG IN THE PALACE SO BUILT BY MAYA AS TO CAUSE ILLUSIONS.

OH! I THOUGHT IT WAS THE FLOOR.

"MANY PEOPLE INCLUDING BHEEMA AND THE QUEENS BURST INTO LAUGHTER AT DURYODHANA'S PLIGHT.

I'LL TEACH THEM A LESSON ONE DAY.

ALTHOUGH YUDHISHTHIRA TRIED TO RESTRAIN THEM, EVERYONE AT THE COURT OF INDRAPRASTHA LAUGHED AND MOCKED AT DURYODHANA. THUS YUDHISHTHIRA'S RAJASOOYA YAJNA WAS HAILED BY EVERY- ONE EXCEPT DURYODHANA, WHOSE HEART WAS FILLED WITH ENVY AND BITTERNESS.

THUS ENDS THE EIGHTH SESSION OF OUR RENDERING OF THE TENTH CHAPTER OF THE BHAGAWAT PURANA.

KRISHNA: THE SAVIOUR

SHUKADEVA WAS NARRATING TO PAREEKSHIT THE EVENTS FOLLOWING THE RAJASOOYA YAJNA OF YUDHISHTHIRA.

WHILE KRISHNA WAS AT INDRAPRASTHA, DWARAKA WAS ATTACKED BY SHALVA.

WHY DID HE DO THAT?

"SHALVA WAS A FRIEND OF SHISHUPALA'S AND HAD ACCOMPANIED HIM TO THE SWAYAMVARA OF RUKMINI. WHEN KRISHNA DEFEATED THEM ALL AND TOOK AWAY RUKMINI, SHALVA HAD VOWED—

I WILL DESTROY ALL THE YADAVAS ONE DAY. JUST WAIT AND SEE.

"HE THEN BEGAN A SEVERE PENANCE. AFTER HE HAD PRACTISED AUSTERITIES FOR A YEAR, LORD SHIVA APPEARED BEFORE HIM.

I WANT A VEHICLE TO ATTACK THE YADAVAS. IT SHOULD BE ABLE TO TRAVEL ANYWHERE—IN AIR, WATER OR ON LAND AND IT MUST BE INDESTRUCTIBLE.

YOUR WISH WILL BE FULFILLED.

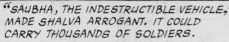

"SAUBHA, THE INDESTRUCTIBLE VEHICLE, MADE SHALVA ARROGANT. IT COULD CARRY THOUSANDS OF SOLDIERS.

IT CAN TAKE ME WHEREVER I WISH TO GO. I AM INVINCIBLE NOW.

"WHEN HE HEARD OF HIS FRIEND, SHISHUPALA'S DEATH, HE BECAME FURIOUS. SEATED IN SAUBHA, HE ATTACKED DWARAKA.

"THOUSANDS OF SOLDIERS GOT DOWN FROM THE VEHICLE AND SURROUNDED THE CITY.

"FROM HIS AIRBORNE VEHICLE, SHALVA RAINED DOWN STRANGE OBJECTS ON THE CITIZENS BELOW.

RUN! HUGE STONES, SERPENTS AND TREES ARE RAINING DOWN FROM THE SKIES!

THERE IS SO MUCH OF DUST AROUND US THAT WE CAN HARDLY SEE A THING.

"IN THE ABSENCE OF KRISHNA, HIS BRAVE SON PRADYUMNA TOOK CHARGE.

KRISHNA IS NOT HERE TO SAVE US.

HELP! WE ARE BEING ATTACKED

DO NOT BE AFRAID. WE WILL PROTECT YOU.

"FOLLOWED BY HIS BROTHERS AND OTHER BRAVE YADAVA WARRIORS, PRADYUMNA MET SHALVA'S ARMY IN A FIERCE BATTLE.

"WELL VERSED AS HE WAS IN THE ART OF USING CELESTIAL WEAPONS, PRADYUMNA DESTROYED THE ILLUSIONS CREATED BY SHALVA.

"WITH HIS SHARP, IRON-TIPPED ARROWS, HE WOUNDED SHALVA'S COMMANDER AS WELL AS HIS SOLDIERS.

"BUT SHALVA IN HIS AIR BORNE VEHICLE APPEARED TO BE INVINCIBLE. THE VEHICLE WOULD MAGICALLY DISAPPEAR...

"...AND THEN SUDDENLY APPEAR IN ANOTHER SPOT. ONE MINUTE IT WOULD BE FLYING THROUGH THE AIR, THE NEXT IT WOULD BE IN WATER.

"WHENEVER IT WAS SIGHTED, THE YADAVAS SHOT A VOLLEY OF ARROWS AT IT CAUSING MUCH DISTRESS TO SHALVA AND HIS SOLDIERS.

"AT LAST THEIR ARROWS FOUND THEIR MARK AND SHALVA FELL INTO A FAINT.

"NOW DYUMAN, A MINISTER OF SHALVA, ATTACKED PRADYUMNA.

GOT YOU!

"PRADYUMNA'S CHARIOTEER CARRIED HIM AWAY FROM THE SPOT.

MY MASTER HAS FAINTED. IT IS MY DUTY TO TAKE HIM AWAY TO SAFETY.

"WHEN PRADYUMNA REGAINED CONSCIOUSNESS, HE WAS FURIOUS.

WHY DID YOU BRING ME AWAY FROM THE BATTLEFIELD? HAS ANY YADAVA EVER RUN AWAY FROM BATTLE? HOW CAN I FACE MY PEOPLE NOW?

BUT IT WAS MY DUTY TO PROTECT YOU, WHEN YOU WERE UNCONSCIOUS.

LET US GO BACK AT ONCE.

"BACK IN THE BATTLE, PRADYUMNA ATTACKED DYUMAN WITH RENEWED VIGOUR.

"SOON, DYUMAN'S HORSES AND CHARIOT WERE DESTROYED. FINALLY THE BRAVE DYUMAN TOO FELL.

"MEANWHILE THE OTHER YADAVA WARRIORS INCLUDING GADA, SATYAKI AND SAMBA, KEPT UP THEIR ATTACK ON SHALVA'S FORCES AND DECIMATED THEIR SOLDIERS, WHO WERE RAINING ARROWS ON THEM FROM THE AIRBORNE VEHICLE. FOR TWENTY-SEVEN LONG DAYS, THE FIERCE BATTLE CONTINUED.

"WHEN KRISHNA AND BALARAMA RETURNED FROM INDRAPRASTHA, THEY FOUND THEIR BELOVED CITY DWARAKA UNDER SIEGE.

"AS SOON AS HE SAW KRISHNA, SHALVA AIMED THE POWERFUL WEAPON, SHAKTI, AT DARUKA, KRISHNA'S CHARIOTEER.

"BUT KRISHNA'S ARROWS REDUCED IT TO A THOUSAND BITS."

"LIKE THE SUN'S RAYS PERVADING THROUGH THE DARK SKIES, KRISHNA'S SHARP ARROWS PENETRATED SHALVA'S WONDROUS VEHICLE."

"SHALVA HIT KRISHNA'S LEFT SHOULDER."

KRISHNA IS HIT.

HIS SHARNGA BOW HAS FALLEN DOWN.

YOU KIDNAPPED SHISHUPALA'S WIFE* AND YOU KILLED HIM TOO. YOU THINK YOU ARE INVINCIBLE, DO YOU? JUST WAIT,

FOOL, USE YOUR WEAPONS, NOT YOUR TONGUE.

KRISHNA HURLED HIS MACE AND HIT SHALVA ON HIS COLLAR BONE...

...AND THE MACE RETURNED TO KRISHNA.

* REFERENCE TO RUKMINI, WHO WAS BETROTHED TO SHISHUPALA.

"SHALVA WAS BADLY INJURED BUT WITH HIS MAGIC VEHICLE, HE SUDDENLY DISAPPEARED.

"SOON A MESSENGER RUSHED TO KRISHNA, WITH TEARS IN HIS EYES.

KRISHNA! KRISHNA! YOUR MOTHER DEVAKI HAS SENT ME. SHALVA HAS CAPTURED YOUR FATHER VASUDEVA.

"KRISHNA BECAME SAD LIKE AN ORDINARY MORTAL.

HOW COULD SHALVA OVERPOWER BALARAMA AND KIDNAP MY FATHER?

"SHALVA THEN REAPPEARED CLASPING VASUDEVA.

SEE! HERE IS YOUR DEAR FATHER. I WILL BEHEAD HIM BEFORE YOUR VERY EYES.

"BEFORE KRISHNA COULD LIFT HIS BOW, SHALVA CUT OFF THE HEAD OF VASUDEVA AND FLED WITH IT BACK INTO HIS VEHICLE, SAUBHA.

"WHEN KRISHNA RECOVERED FROM THE SHOCK HE REALISED THAT THE WHOLE INCIDENT HAD BEEN AN ILLUSION.

IT HAS ALL DISAPPEARED LIKE A DREAM: THE MESSENGER, AND THE BODY OF MY FATHER. IT WAS A CREATION OF SHALVA'S MAYA*

"ENRAGED, KRISHNA ATTACKED SHALVA'S VEHICLE WITH HIS MACE, TILL IT SHATTERED TO BITS AND FELL INTO THE OCEAN.

"BUT IN THE NICK OF TIME, SHALVA JUMPED OFF TO CONFRONT KRISHNA."

"KRISHNA NOW RELEASED HIS SUDARSHANA CHAKRA**...

AND CUT OFF SHALVA'S HEAD.

* ILLUSORY POWER ** DISC

"DANTAVAKRA, ANOTHER FRIEND OF SHISHUPALA'S, ARRIVED ON THE BATTLE FIELD JUST THEN.

I MUST AVENGE THE DEATH OF MY FRIENDS—SHISHUPALA, PAUNDRAKA AND SHALVA.

"THOUGH HE WAS ARMED WITH ONLY A MACE, DANTAVAKRA'S HEAVY STEPS MADE THE VERY EARTH TREMBLE.

THE ONLY WAY I CAN DO IT IS BY KILLING YOU.

" BUT IN SPITE OF THE HEAVY BLOW, KRISHNA WAS UNRUFFLED. TAKING CAREFUL AIM, HE HIT DANTAVAKRA ON THE CHEST...

...KILLING HIM THAT VERY MOMENT.

" NOW VIDURATHA, THE BROTHER OF DANTAVAKRA ENTERED THE FRAY...

... BUT HE TOO WAS SOON KILLED.

" THE VICTORIOUS YADAVA ARMY ENTERED THE CITY AMIDST JOYOUS CHEERING.

IT WAS AFTER THIS INCIDENT THAT SUDAMA VISITED KRISHNA.

WHO WAS SUDAMA?

" SUDAMA WAS A BRAHMIN WHO HAD BEEN A CHILDHOOD FRIEND OF KRISHNA.

"THE YEARS THAT HAD ROLLED BY HAD NOT BEEN KIND TO SUDAMA. HE AND HIS WIFE LIVED IN DIRE POVERTY.

"THOUGH SHE WAS ALWAYS IN TATTERED CLOTHES AND STARVING, FOR LONG SUDAMA'S WIFE BORE HER SUFFERING PATIENTLY. ONE DAY —

YOU TOLD ME THAT KRISHNA, THE LORD OF DWARAKA, IS YOUR FRIEND.

SO HE IS.

WHY DON'T YOU GO AND MEET HIM? WHEN HE COMES TO KNOW THAT YOU HAVE A FAMILY TO SUPPORT, HE WILL SURELY HELP YOU.

"SUDAMA'S WIFE REPEATEDLY REQUESTED HIM TO GO TO KRISHNA.

THE VERY THOUGHT OF MEETING MY FRIEND KRISHNA MAKES ME HAPPY. INDEED I MUST GO.

IS THERE ANYTHING IN THE HOUSE WHICH I CAN TAKE AS A GIFT?

WAIT!

"QUICKLY SHE COLLECTED A FEW HANDFUL OF POWA* FROM HER NEIGHBOURS.

HERE, TAKE THIS.

" WITH THE SMALL BUNDLE, SUDAMA SET OUT FOR DWARAKA.

I JUST CAN'T WAIT TO MEET KRISHNA.

AT LAST HE REACHED DWARAKA. HE FOUND KRISHNA IN RUKMINI'S BEAUTIFUL PALACE.

MY DEAR SUDAMA!

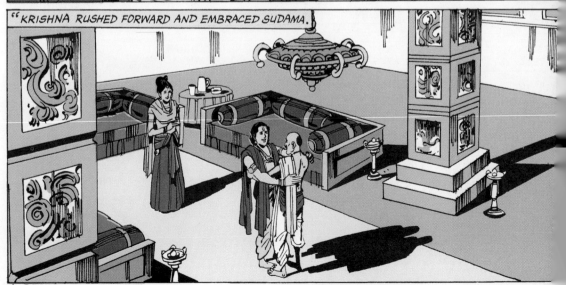

"KRISHNA RUSHED FORWARD AND EMBRACED SUDAMA.

* BEATEN RICE

COME, SIT HERE.

"WITH HIS OWN HANDS KRISHNA BATHED SUDAMA'S FEET, WHILE RUKMINI GENTLY FANNED HIM.

"RUKMINI'S MAIDS WERE ASTONISHED AT THE SIGHT.

HOW CAN OUR LORD KRISHNA DO THIS?

THAT MAN LOOKS SO WOEBEGONE AND DIRTY.

HE IS ALL SKIN AND BONES, LOOKS LIKE A BEGGAR.

"HOLDING SUDAMA'S HAND AFFECTIONATELY, KRISHNA BEGAN TO TALK OF THE OLD DAYS.

DO YOU REMEMBER OUR DAYS AT THE GURUKULA? THE DAY WE WERE SENT TO THE FOREST TO COLLECT FIRE-WOOD...

DO YOU REMEMBER THE TERRIBLE STORM THAT SUDDENLY BROKE OUT?

"THE WHOLE FOREST BECAME DARK AND FLOODED, AND WE HELD ON TO EACH OTHER AND SPENT THE FEARFUL NIGHT THERE."

"WHEN OUR GURU SANDIPANI FOUND US IN THE FOREST AT DAWN, HE WAS SO TOUCHED."

YOU RISKED YOUR LIVES FOR OUR SAKE. MAY ALL YOUR WISHES COME TRUE. MAY YOU NEVER LOSE THE KNOWLEDGE YOU HAVE ACQUIRED

INDEED I WAS FORTUNATE TO BE WITH YOU AT THE GURUKUL.

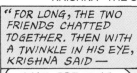

"FOR LONG, THE TWO FRIENDS CHATTED TOGETHER. THEN WITH A TWINKLE IN HIS EYE, KRISHNA SAID —

WHAT PRESENT HAVE YOU BROUGHT ME?

"HE SAW SUDAMA HESITATING.

WHEN MY TRUE DEVOTEES OFFER THE SMALLEST GIFTS WITH LOVE. I FEEL PLEASED.

ON THE OTHER HAND, RICH EXPENSIVE PRESENTS OFFERED TO ME WITHOUT ANY DEVOTION HAVE NO MEANING FOR ME.

COME, SHOW ME WHAT YOU HAVE BROUGHT.

NO, NOTHING.

AH! GOT IT.

WHY, IT'S POWA! MY FAVOURITE FOOD!

"BEFORE HE COULD EAT THE SECOND FISTFUL, RUKMINI INTERVENED —

THAT IS ENOUGH, MY LORD! IT IS SUFFICIENT TO GIVE A MAN ALL HE NEEDS IN THIS WORLD AND THE NEXT.

"SUDAMA SPENT THE NIGHT IN KRISHNA'S PALACE.

WHAT COMFORT AND LUXURY! I FEEL I AM IN HEAVEN.

"ALTHOUGH HE HAD ASKED FOR NOTHING AND RECEIVED NOTHING FROM KRISHNA, SUDAMA WAS HAPPY WHEN HE LEFT NEXT MORNING.

HOW LUCKY I AM. LORD KRISHNA TREATED ME AS IF I WERE HIS BROTHER.

THOUGH HE IS FAMED FOR HIS GENEROSITY, HE PURPOSELY DID NOT GIVE ME WEALTH.

HE KNOWS THAT SUDDEN WEALTH CAN TURN A POOR MAN'S HEAD AND MAKE HIM FORGETFUL OF GOD AND HIS DUTY.

"WHEN HE REACHED HIS VILLAGE AT LAST—

I MUST HAVE LOST MY WAY. I HAVE NEVER SEEN SUCH A WONDERFUL PALACE BEFORE.

"INDEED IT WAS A STUNNING SIGHT— A RESPLENDENT PALACE STUDDED WITH PRECIOUS STONES. IN ITS BEAUTIFULLY LAID GARDENS WERE COLOURFUL BIRDS, AND PONDS FILLED WITH LOTUSES.

"JUST THEN, SUDAMA'S WIFE CAME OUT FROM THE PALACE TO RECEIVE HIM. THERE WAS A BIG RETINUE OF SERVANTS.

I CAN HARDLY RECOGNIZE YOU IN THESE FINE CLOTHES AND GOLD ORNAMENTS.

COME AND SEE INSIDE.

"THE INTERIOR OF THE PALACE WAS FILLED WITH FURNITURE OF GOLD AND IVORY. THE PILLARS WERE STUDDED WITH PRECIOUS STONES.

ALL THIS CAN ONLY BE THROUGH THE BENEVOLENCE OF KRISHNA.

I DID NOT ASK HIM ANYTHING BUT HE MUST HAVE GUESSED WHAT WAS IN MY MIND.

"AMIDST THE SPLENDOUR, SUDAMA CONTINUED HIS SIMPLE LIFE.

MAY MY MIND CONTINUE TO DWELL ON HIS GLORY AND GREATNESS.

WHILE KRISHNA AND BALARAMA WERE IN DWARAKA, A TOTAL ECLIPSE OF THE SUN WAS PREDICTED. AS TRADITION DEMANDED, THE YADAVAS DECIDED TO GO TO THE HOLY SPOT OF SAMANTAPANCHAKA AT KURUKSHETRA, LEAVING ANIRUDDHA AND THE ARMY COMMANDER KRITAVARMA IN CHARGE OF DWARAKA.

"WHEN, BEDECKED IN THEIR FINEST GARMENTS, FLOWERS AND ORNAMENTS, THEY REACHED KURUKSHETRA, THEY FOUND THE KINGS OF VARIOUS REGIONS ASSEMBLED THERE.

"THEY WERE DELIGHTED TO BEHOLD NANDA, YASHODA AND OTHER KINSMEN. THE KAURAVAS AND PANDAVAS WERE ALSO THERE.

"IT WAS A SCENE OF JOYOUS REUNION. THE GOPIS* BEHELD THEIR DEAR KRISHNA AFTER A LONG TIME AND WERE DELIGHTED BY THE MERE SIGHT OF HIM.

"THE WOMEN FOLK OF THE YADAVA AND THE KAURAVA CLANS CHATTED EXCITEDLY.

DO TELL US HOW KRISHNA MARRIED YOU.

"ONE BY ONE, SATYABHAMA, RUKMINI, JAMBAVATI, SATYA, KALINDI, LAKSHMANA, MITRAVINDA AND BHADRA NARRATED THE EXCITING EVENTS LEADING TO THEIR MARRIAGE WITH KRISHNA.

" DRAUPADI WAS SURPRISED TO HEAR LAKSHMANA'S TALE.

MY SWAYAMVARA WAS QUITE SIMILAR TO YOURS. THE CONTESTANTS HAD TO SHOOT A FISH, REVOLVING AT A HEIGHT, BY LOOKING AT ITS REFLECTION IN A VESSEL OF OIL.

YES! YES! THAT WAS THE TEST BY WHICH ARJUNA WON MY HAND.†

✶ COWHERDESSES   † MAHABHARATA GIVES A DIFFERENT VERSION OF THIS.

"LAKSHMANA CONTINUED —

BUT IN MY CASE, THAT FISH WAS COVERED AND WAS NOT DIRECTLY VISIBLE TO THE ARCHER. HE COULD SEE ONLY ITS REFLECTION.

MANY BRAVE MEN INCLUDING DURYODHANA, JARASANDHA, SHISHUPALA AND KARNA TRIED THEIR HAND BUT THEY COULD NOT FELL THE FISH. BUT KRISHNA DID IT SO EFFORTLESSLY.

"DRAUPADI, KUNTI AND GANDHARI WERE MOVED TO HEAR THE DEVOTION SHOWN TO KRISHNA BY HIS MANY WIVES.

JUST THEN MANY REVERED RISHIS, INCLUDING VEDA VYASA, NARADA AND VISHWAMITRA CAME THERE.

"AFTER THEY WERE RECEIVED WITH DUE HONOUR AND CEREMONY, KRISHNA SAID —

BLESSED ARE WE TO BEHOLD SO MANY GREAT MEN AT A TIME FOR IT IS NOT BY VISITING HOLY PLACES OR WORSHIPPING CLAY IMAGES THAT ONE GAINS SALVATION.

HE WHO IDENTIFIES HIMSELF WITH HIS BODY AND NOT WITH THE SOUL IS AN ASS. SO IS THE PERSON WHO CONSIDERS THE WATER OF THE RIVER MORE IMPORTANT THAN THE GREAT RISHIS AND WISE MEN GATHERED AT SUCH PLACES OF PILGRIMAGE.

"AT FIRST THE RISHIS, WHO HAD COME TO OFFER WORSHIP TO KRISHNA, WERE SURPRISED BY THE REVERENCE SHOWN BY KRISHNA. THEN REALISATION DAWNED ON THEM.

O LORD, YOU REVEL IN BEHAVING LIKE AN ORDINARY MORTAL. LET ALONE THE KINGS GATHERED HERE, EVEN THE PEOPLE WHO ARE CLOSEST TO YOU ARE UNAWARE OF YOUR DIVINE FORM.

"AFTER OFFERING HOMAGE TO KRISHNA, THE RISHIS WERE ABOUT TO TAKE LEAVE WHEN VASUDEVA STOPPED THEM.

I HAVE A FAVOUR TO ASK. INSTRUCT ME HOW I CAN RID MYSELF OF SIN-FULNESS.

"NARADA SAID IN A WHISPERED UNDERTONE TO HIS COMPANION RISHIS.

IS IT NOT STRANGE THAT HE IS IGNORANT OF THE GREATNESS OF HIS SON KRISHNA AND ASKS US FOR ADVICE? INDEED PROXIMITY DOES LEAD TO INDIFFERENCE.

"ALOUD HE SAID—

YOU SHOULD WORSHIP LORD VISHNU BY PERFORMING A YAJNA.

"UNDER THE GUIDANCE OF THE RISHIS, VASUDEVA BEGAN A YAJNA AT THE HOLY SPOT.

"AFTER APPLYING CORYLLIUM IN HIS EYES AND SMEARING HIS BODY WITH BUTTER, VASUDEVA PERFORMED THE YAJNA DRESSED IN DEERSKIN WHILE HIS WIVES WERE DECKED IN SILKEN GARMENTS AND BEJEWELLED ORNAMENTS.

"AFTER THE YAJNA, VASUDEVA GAVE GENEROUS GIFTS TO THE RISHIS AND THE ASSEMBLED KINGS. KRISHNA, BALARAMA AND UGRASENA WORSHIPPED NANDA AND OTHER GOPAS AND SHOWERED THEM WITH GIFTS.

NANDA! I AM EVER INDEBTED TO YOU FOR TAKING CARE OF MY CHILDREN WHEN THEY WERE YOUNG.

"WITH HEAVY HEARTS, YUDHISHTHIRA AND HIS BROTHERS TOOK LEAVE OF KRISHNA.

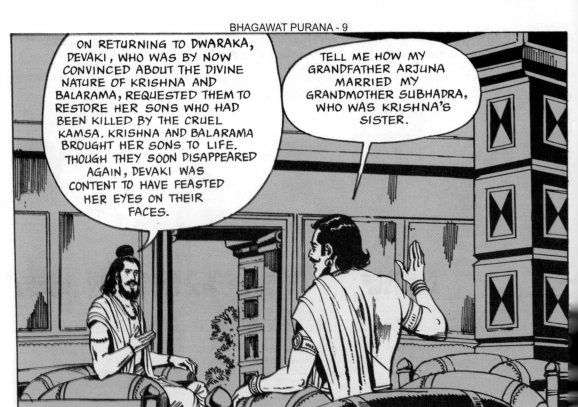

ON RETURNING TO DWARAKA, DEVAKI, WHO WAS BY NOW CONVINCED ABOUT THE DIVINE NATURE OF KRISHNA AND BALARAMA, REQUESTED THEM TO RESTORE HER SONS WHO HAD BEEN KILLED BY THE CRUEL KAMSA. KRISHNA AND BALARAMA BROUGHT HER SONS TO LIFE. THOUGH THEY SOON DISAPPEARED AGAIN, DEVAKI WAS CONTENT TO HAVE FEASTED HER EYES ON THEIR FACES.

TELL ME HOW MY GRANDFATHER ARJUNA MARRIED MY GRANDMOTHER SUBHADRA, WHO WAS KRISHNA'S SISTER.

"ONCE WHILE ARJUNA WAS ON A YEAR'S PILGRIMAGE AROUND THE COUNTRY HE ARRIVED AT PRABHASA.

HAVE YOU HEARD? BALARAMA IS PLANNING TO MARRY HIS BEAUTIFUL SISTER SUBHADRA TO DURYODHANA.

BUT KRISHNA AND VASUDEVA DO NOT AGREE TO THIS ALLIANCE.

"ARJUNA HAD HEARD ABOUT SUBHADRA'S UNSURPASSED BEAUTY AND CHARM.

THEN I MUST GO TO DWARAKA.

"DISGUISED AS A SANYASI, HE REACHED DWARAKA. HE DECIDED TO SPEND FOUR MONTHS OF THE RAINY SEASON THERE."

"BELIEVING HIM TO BE AN ASCETIC, BALARAMA INVITED HIM FOR A MEAL TO HIS PALACE."

"IT WAS THEN THAT ARJUNA FIRST BEHELD SUBHADRA WHO, ACCORDING TO TRADITION WAITED ON THE HONOURED GUESTS."

HOW LOVELY SHE LOOKS.

"SUBHADRA TOO WAS SMITTEN BY LOVE FOR THE HANDSOME FORM OF ARJUNA*"

I WILL MARRY NONE OTHER.

ACCORDING TO A MAHABHARATA VERSION, ARJUNA REVEALS HIS REAL IDENTITY TO HER.

"FROM THAT MOMENT, ARJUNA'S HEART KNEW NO PEACE.

I MUST CARRY HER AWAY AND MAKE HER MY WIFE.

"ARJUNA TOOK KRISHNA AND VASUDEVA INTO CONFIDENCE. ONE DAY SUBHADRA WAS GOING TO THE TEMPLE OUTSIDE THE CITY GATES.

"ARJUNA WAS WAITING FOR THIS MOMENT. SWIFTLY HE CARRIED SUBHADRA TO HIS OWN CHARIOT.

"WHEN THE YADAVA SOLDIERS PURSUED THEM, ARJUNA REPELLED THEM WITH EASE.

SUBHADRA IS KIDNAPPED!

LOOK! HE IS TAKING HER AWAY.

"BALARAMA WAS FURIOUS.

HOW DARE HE DO SO!

"IT WAS KRISHNA WHO PACIFIED BALARAMA AND MADE HIM AGREE TO THE ALLIANCE. HE THEN ARRANGED FOR RICH PRESENTS TO BE SENT TO THE NEWLY-WEDS.

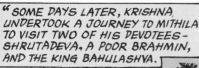

"SOME DAYS LATER, KRISHNA UNDERTOOK A JOURNEY TO MITHILA TO VISIT TWO OF HIS DEVOTEES - SHRUTADEVA, A POOR BRAHMIN, AND THE KING BAHULASHVA.

"WHEN THEY HEARD OF HIS ARRIVAL, BOTH DEVOTEES RUSHED TO GREET KRISHNA.

DO COME TO MY HUMBLE HOME, O LORD.

YOU MUST ACCEPT MY HOSPITALITY, LORD.

THEY ARE EQUALLY DEVOTED TO ME. I CANNOT DISAPPOINT EITHER OF THEM.

"KRISHNA ASSUMED TWO DIFFERENT FORMS AND VISITED BOTH THEIR HOUSES AT THE SAME TIME.

" WHILE THE KING OF VIDEHA, BAHULASHVA, OFFERED KRISHNA LUXURIOUS SEATS AND WORSHIPPED HIM WITH FLOWERS, GARMENTS, OFFERINGS OF ORNAMENTS AND CATTLE...

" SHRUTADEVA QUICKLY MADE A SEAT OF GRASS, AND OFFERED KRISHNA SIMPLE FRUITS AND FLOWERS.

" PLEASED WITH THEIR SINCERE DEVOTION, KRISHNA SPENT SOME DAYS IN THEIR HOUSES, ENLIGHTENING THEM WITH HIS DISCOURSES.

SHUKADEVA SAID—

THUS IT WAS THAT KRISHNA, AN INCARNATION OF VISHNU, LIVED IN THE WORLD LIKE AN ORDINARY HOUSEHOLDER, UPHOLDING DHARMA AND FULFILLING THE PURPOSE OF HIS INCARNATION.

BY LISTENING, RECITING AND MEDITATING ON THE THEME OF KRISHNA, A MORTAL CAN HOPE TO ACHIEVE SALVATION.

THUS ENDS THE LAST SESSION OF OUR RENDERING OF THE TENTH CHAPTER OF THE BHAGAWAT PURANA